Xmas, '23

RECITATION IN COSTUME

SONG OF THE FLOWER GIRL

BOYS' AND GIRLS' SPEAKER

THE CHOICEST RECITATIONS AND READINGS FROM THE BEST AUTHORS FOR PUBLIC SCHOOLS, PARLOR ENTERTAINMENTS and SOCIAL GATHERINGS. RECITALS IN PROSE AND VERSE. SELECTIONS WITH MUSICAL ACCOMPANIMENTS, DIALOGUES, TABLEAUX, Etc.

COMPILED AND EDITED BY

HENRY DAVENPORT NORTHROP

Author of "Crown Jewels," "Beautiful Gems," Etc.

EMBELLISHED WITH COPPERPLATE ETCHINGS AND LINE DRAWINGS

PREFACE.

THERE is an immense and constantly growing demand for the very best selections from the best authors for readings and recitations. No form of entertainment is more universally popular than this for Schools, Social gatherings, Lyceums, Lodges, Church and Sunday-school Anniversaries, Christmas Exhibitions and many other public occasions. The cultured voice and magnetic personality of the successful reader are always charming and welcome.

This demand is fully supplied by this work, which is a rich casket of gems in Prose and Poetry, all strikingly adapted to instruct and entertain. They are suited to every conceivable occasion where a reading is in order, and are the best afforded by the whole range of literature, comprising Eloquence and Sentiment; Pathos and Humor; Dramatic and Descriptive Selections; Juvenile Readings, Dialogues, Tableaux, etc., etc.

The Illustrated Broom Drill, with which the work begins, furnishes an excellent exercise for young people. It keeps the body erect, requires a great variety of positions, develops all the muscles and teaches the easy, graceful use of the body. In this part of the work is a great variety of Selections which young people find suitable for readings and recitations on every occasion.

These and all the other pieces the book contains have been selected with the greatest care. Their moral tone is elevating, and this renders them such selections as no parent or teacher would hesitate to put into the hands of the young. The prevailing character of this part of the work is dramatic, affording an excellent opportunity for the best display of ability in the reader's consummate art.

A very choice collection of Dialogues adds greatly to the value of this volume. There is often great difficulty in obtaining suitable dialogues for public occasions, such as exhibitions and anniversaries.

iii

Those which are here presented afford a wide scope for the varied talents of young persons. Some of them are humorous, and contain playful hits at prevalent follies. Full instructions are given for preparing the stage and presenting the drama in the most effective manner.

A collection of short pieces is entitled Encores. These are short and pithy, and such as may be delivered when one, having made a success of his reading, is called out for a second performance. These may also be used as first selections for any entertainment.

Recognizing the fact that Humorous Readings are always popular, the editor of this volume has devoted to them a large space. Here are presented the best things by humorous writers of world-wide fame, such as Dickens, Burdette, Charles Adams, Mark Twain, Eugene Field, etc. These selections, when recited, are always received with bursts of merriment and applause. Very often the success of a recitation does not come from any special merit on the part of the reciter, but from the quaint and humorous character of the reading itself. A glance at this part of the volume will convince every one that it could not be improved. Strange happenings, laughable mistakes, playful incidents and grotesque situations are all described. In short, the whole work is bright and cheery, and is an excellent volume for ordinary reading. It should be in the hands of every young person in America.

CONTENTS.

RECITATIONS FOR JUVENILES.

ENCORES.

DIALOGUES AND TABLEAUX.

HUMOROUS READINGS.

RECITATIONS FOR JUVENILES.

DRILLS and marches by the little folks are always in order. The preparation for these benefits young people by requiring them to move the body quickly and gracefully, assuming an erect attitude, then other positions at the word of command. Such exercises also aid in forming a habit of strict attention.

The Broom Drill is one of the most entertaining, and can readily be learned. It should be practiced until it can be performed promptly and without any mistakes. Twelve or sixteen girls—in fact, any even number, according to the size of the stage—may take part in it.

All should be dressed alike, in blouse waist of Turkey red chintz, sleeves and collar trimmed with white braid; skirt made of white cheese cloth, trimmed above the hem with band of red chintz, four or five inches wide; a red cap completes the costume.

During the marching there should be music, and the notes of the piano should be struck sharply. Any good march will answer for the music.

The following exercises conform very nearly to the "Manual of Arms" used in the army. The cuts will be found very serviceable in showing the different positions.

2 & C.

THE BROOM DRILL.

STANDING in rank near the front side of the stage, the teacher gives the command to "present arms," "carry arms," "trail arms," etc. Each command consists of two words: the first is to indicate what the pupil is to do, and on the second word the movement is made, all acting in concert.

The following exercises are suitable for this drill, and always prove very entertaining to the audience.

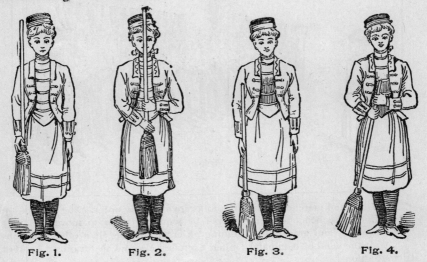

Fig. 1.   Fig. 2.   Fig. 3.   Fig. 4.

Carry—ARMS!—The broom is held in the right hand, handle upward, with the hand clasping the handle where it joins the brush. The left hand hangs at the side. (Fig. 1.)

Present—ARMS!—Place the broom with the right hand in front of the centre of the body, clasping the handle with the left hand above the right. Hold the broom perfectly perpendicular. (Fig. 2.)

Order—ARMS!—Let go the handle with the left hand, and carry the broom to the side with the right hand; then drop the broom to the floor. (Fig. 3.)

In place—REST!—Grasp the handle with both hands, the left above the right, and place both hands in front of the lower part of the breast. (Fig. 4.)

Trail—ARMS !—Grasp the handle with the right hand and incline it forward, the broom behind, resting on the floor. (Fig. 5.)

Attention—CHARGE !—Half face to the right, carrying the heel six inches to the rear and three inches to the right of the left, turning the toes of both feet slightly inward ; at the same time drop the stick into the left hand, elbow against the body, point of stick at the height of the chin, right hand grasping the stick just above the brush and supporting it firmly against the right hip. (Fig. 6.)

Fig. 5.   Fig. 6.   Fig. 7.   Fig. 8.

Port—ARMS !—Raise and throw the broom diagonally across the body ; grasp it smartly with both hands, the right, palm down at the base of the stick ; the left, palm up, thumb clasping stick ; handle sloping to the left and crossing opposite the middle of left shoulder ; right forearm horizontal ; forearms and handle near the body. (Fig. 7.)

Secure—ARMS !—Advance the broom slightly with the right hand, turn the handle to the front with the left hand. At the same time change the position of the right hand, placing it further up the handle, drop the handle to the front, placing the broom where joined with the handle, under the right arm. (Fig. 8.)

Reverse—ARMS !—Lift the broom vertically with the right hand, clasp the stick with the left hand ; then, with the right hand, grasp the handle near the brush. Reverse the broom, the handle dropping to the front, the broom passing between the breast and right forearm. Press the handle under the arm with the left hand until the right elbow can hold it in place against the body ; pass left hand behind the back and clasp the stick. (Fig. 9.)

Fig. 9.   Fig. 10.   Fig. 11.

Inspection—ARMS !—This is executed from the "carry arms" position. Lift the broom quickly with the right hand, bringing it in front of the centre of the body ; then grasp the handle with the left hand, placed near the chin, and hold it. (Fig. 10.)

MOVEMENTS OF ATTACK AND DEFENSE.

These can be executed only with open ranks, the pupils being placed seven or eight feet apart. To so place them, the teacher will give the order—

Right (or Left) open Ranks—MARCH !—The pupils face to the right or left, according to the order given, except the one at the extreme end of the

One. The others march, the last of the file halting at every four or five steps from the one in the rear, until all are the same distance apart. They then face front. To close the rank, turn to the right or left and march toward the pupil standing at the end until halted by the one ahead. Then face front.

Attention—GUARD!—At the command *guard*, half face to the right, carry back and place the right foot about twice its length to the rear and nearly the same distance to the right, the feet at little less than a right angle, the right toe pointing squarely to the right, both knees bent slightly, weight of the body held equally on both legs; at the same time throw the end of the stick to the front, at the height of the chin, grasping it lightly with both hands, the right just above the brush, the left a few inches higher; the right hand in line with the left hip and both arms held free from the body and without constraint. (Fig. 11.)

Being at the Guard—ADVANCE!—Move the left foot quickly forward, twice its length; follow with the right foot the same distance.

RETIRE!—Move the right foot quickly to the rear, twice its length; follow with the left foot the same distance.

Front—PASS!—Advance the right foot quickly, fifteen inches in front of the left, keeping right toe squarely to the right; advance the left foot to its relative position in front.

Rear—PASS!—Carry the left foot quickly fifteen inches to the rear of the right; place the right foot in its relative position in rear, keeping the right toe squarely to the right.

Right—VOLT!—Face to the right, turning on the ball of the left foot, at the same time carry the right foot quickly to its position in rear.

Left—VOLT!—Face to the left, turning on the ball of the left foot, at the same time carry the right foot quickly to its position in rear.

Right rear and left rear volts are similarly executed, facing about on the ball of the left foot.

Quarte—PARRY!—Hold the broom in front of the left shoulder with the right hand, handle upward, the fingers of the left hand on the handle, the left elbow touching the right wrist. (Fig. 12.)

Seconde—PARRY !—Move the point of the broom-handle quickly to the left, describing a semi-circle from left to right, the left elbow in front of the body, the flat of the broom under the right forearm, the right elbow two or three inches higher than the right shoulder.　(Fig. 13.)

Fig. 12.　　　　Fig. 13.　　　　Fig. 14.

Prime—PARRY.—Carry the broom to the left, covering the left shoulder, the handle downward, the left forearm behind the handle, the right arm in front of and above the eyes.　(Fig. 14.)

THRUSTS.

To THRUST IN TIERCE.—Straighten the right leg, extend both arms, keeping point of handle at height of the breast, broom at right side of head. (Fig. 15.)

THRUST IN QUARTE.—The same as tierce, but with the broom on the left side of the head.

LUNGES.

The lunges are the same as the thrusts, except that the left foot is extended farther in front.　(Fig. 16.)

Fig. 15.   Fig. 16.

Broom to Front—ONE !—Raise handle nearly straight up and down, drop it into the hollow of the right shoulder.—Two !—Strike quickly by pushing the broom forward, the handle always resting on the right shoulder. (Fig. 17.)

Fig. 17.   Fig. 18.

Right Short—-THRUST !—ONE !—Hold the broom with the right hand to the rear, left hand by the right breast, the point of the handle opposite the centre of the body.—Two !—Thrust forward. (Fig. 18.)

High Prime—PARRY !—Raise the broom with both hands in front of and higher than the head. Hold the handle firmly with the right hand, the broom being to the right; turn the knuckles of the left hand to the front, and let other end of broom-handle rest on the thumb and forefinger. (Fig. 19.)

Fig. 19.   Fig. 20.

TO GUARD WHEN KNEELING.—Bring the toe of the left foot square in front, plant the right foot to the rear, kneel on the right knee, bending the left, hold the broom at an angle of 45 degrees, pointing directly to the front, the right hand pressed firmly against the side, the left hand holding the point of handle upward. (Fig. 20.)

THE MARCH.

[There should be music while the pupils are coming upon the stage and leaving. Any spirited march will answer.]

Girls enter from right and left sides of stage at the back, eight on each side, and march in single files according to the diagram on opposite page. When they meet at C F, separate and march to L F and R F, then up sides of stage to back, then across back to C B. When they meet at C B, form couples and march in twos forward on centre line. At C F first couple turn to R F, second to L F, third to R F, fourth to L F, etc.

"HARK! THE WEDDING BELLS ARE RINGING,
OVER THE HILLS THEIR ECHOES FLINGING."

THE YOUNG PATRIOT

March up sides to back, and when couples meet at C B march in fours to C F. First four turn to R F, second four to L F, etc. March up sides to back.

When the fours meet at C B, form eights and march toward front and halt for drill. During the march they "carry brooms" in the right hand,

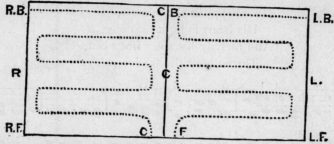

the stick resting against the right shoulder and nearly vertical, the arm hanging at nearly its full length near the body, the hand grasping the handle of the broom just above the sweep (the brush part), which rests flat against the side of skirt. The thumb and forefinger must be in front.

LABOR SONG.

[This is a charming exercise for boys and girls. Each should be dressed in the costume of the character to be represented, and, as far as possible, should go through the motions called for by the part. The properties can all be placed on the stage before the performance begins. Each character comes in alone, those who have already entered remaining until the close. All unite in singing the chorus, after each performer has spoken or sung (according to choice) the part he or she is to act. Music suitable for this selection is herewith furnished.]

THE FARMER (*with scythe and dressed like a farmer*).

I'M glad I am a husbandman,
My acres broad to till,
And in the Autumn of the year
My many barns to fill.
How happy is the farmer's life,
'Tis one of peace and joy,
To reap and sow, and plow and mow,
And thus the time employ.

CHORUS.

How happy is the laborer,
  For when the day is o'er,
The evening shadows gather round,
  That he may work no more;
How happy is the laborer,
  His heart is light and gay,
And merrily his song rings out,
  Throughout the livelong day.

Chorus D C. al Fine.

THE FARMER'S WIFE (*kneading bread*).

I'm glad I am a farmer's wife,
  The wheaten bread to knead,

And when the men come home from work,
  Their hungry mouths to feed.
I keep my house in perfect trim,
  I sweep and dust and bake,
And when the busy day is done,
  Sweet is the rest I take.—CHORUS.

THE FARMER'S GIRL (*with broom and milk pail*).

I'm glad I am a farmer's girl,
  I love the farmer's life,
And if I ever wed at all,
  I'll be a farmer's wife.
My milking pails make music sweet,
  I'm happy all the day,
Work gives my cheek the glow of health,
  And drives dull care away.—CHORUS.

THE FARMER'S BOY (*with rake*).

I'm glad I am a farmer's boy,
  To plant and rake and hoe—
I get upon old Dobbin's back,
  And don't I make him go?
I shout and make the welkin ring,
  I sing my merry song,
And, roaming through the fields and woods,
  I'm jolly all day long.   [*Boy whistles Chorus*

DAIRY MAID (*with churn*).

I'm glad I am a dairy maid,
  My butter is so yellow;
I know the lad that catches me
  Will be a lucky fellow.
I'm glad I am a dairy maid,
  My heart is light and gay

And with my milk and cream and churn,
　I'm happy all the day.——CHORUS.

WASHERWOMAN (*with tub and washboard*).

I'm glad I am a washerwoman,
　Ye know me by mi look,
I'll wash and starch your snowy clothes,
　And fold them like a book;
Then sind me in your orders quick
　For I've no time for fooling;

(*Spoken.*)

I'll do thim to the best of my ability,
　Ontirely sure.——CHORUS.

THE SHOEMAKER (*shoe, last and hammer*).

I'm glad I am a shoemaker,
　With hammer, last and shoe;
Without the slippers that I make,
　What would the ladies do?
I cut the leather, fit the last—
　To me, my work is play—
From morn to night, with heart so light,
　I sing and peg away.——CHORUS.

THE BLACKSMITH (*with anvil and hammer*).

I'm glad I am a blacksmith,
　A noble horse to shoe,
I hold within my lap his hoof,
　And whack the shoe-nail through;
I swing the hammer and I know
　Just how to make a hit,
And indigestion, if you please,
　Don't trouble me a bit.——CHORUS.

THE SCHOOL-TEACHER (*with slate, book and rule ; three or four children to take part of scholars*).

I'm glad I am a school-teacher,
    With slate and book and rule,
To teach the young idea to shoot,
    And extirpate the fool.
The heights of knowledge I point out,
    And upward lead the way,
And with my pupils pressing on,
    I'm happy every day.—CHORUS.

BOYS WANTED.

BOYS of spirit, boys of will,
    Boys of muscle, brain and power,
Fit to cope with anything,
    These are wanted every hour.

Not the weak and whining drones,
    Who all troubles magnify;
Not the watchword of " I can't,
    But the nobler one, " I'll try."

Do whate'er you have to do
    With a true and earnest zeal;
Bend your sinews to the task,
    " Put your shoulder to the wheel."

Though your duty may be hard,
    Look not on it as an ill;
If it be an honest task,
    Do it with an honest will.

In the workshop, on the farm,
    At the desk, where'er you be,
From your future efforts, boys,
    Comes a nation's destiny.

THE TRUE STORY OF LITTLE BOY BLUE.

LITTLE Boy Blue, as the story goes,
    One morning in summer fell fast asleep,
When he should have been, as every one knows,
    Watching the cows and sheep.

Now all of you will remember what
    Came of the nap on that summer morn;
How the sheep got into the meadow-lot,
    And the cows got into the corn.

Neglecting a duty is wrong, of course,
    But I've always felt, if we could but know,
That the matter was made a great deal worse
    Than it should have been, and so

I find in my sifting, that there was one
    Still more to blame than Little Boy Blue.
I am anxious to have full justice done,
    And so, I know, are you.

The one to blame I have found to be
    (I'm sorry to say it) little Bo-Peep;
You will remember, perhaps, that she
    Also was minding sheep.

Well, little Bo-Peep came tripping along—
    (The sheep *she* tended were running at large)—
Where little Boy Blue sat singing a song,
    And faithfully watching his charge.

Said little Bo-Peep, "It's a burning shame
    That you should sit here from week to week.
Just leave your work, and we'll play a game
    Of—well—of hide and seek."

It *was* dull work, and he liked to play
    Better, I'm sure, than to eat or sleep;

    He liked the bloom of the summer day;—
      And he liked—he liked Bo-Peep.

And so, with many a laugh and shout,
    They hid from each other—now here—now there;

And whether the cows were in or out,
  Bo-Peep had never a care.

"I will hide once more," said the maiden fair,
  "You shall not find me this time, I say—
Shut your eyes up tight, and lie down there
  Under that stack of hay.

"Now wait till I call," said Miss Bo-Peep,
  And over the meadows she slipped away,
With never a thought for cows or sheep—
  Alas! Alas! the day.

She let down the bars, did Miss Bo-Peep—
  Such trifles as bars she held in scorn—
And into the meadows went the sheep,
  And the cows went into the corn.

Then long and patiently waited he
  For the blithesome call from her rosy lips;
He waited in vain—quite like, you see,
  The boy on the burning ship.

And by and by, when they found Boy Blue
  In the merest dose, *he* took the blame.
I think it was fine in him—don't you—
  Not to mention Bo-Peep's name?

And thus it has happened that all these years
  He has borne the blame she ought to share.
Since I know the truth of it, it appears
  To me to be only fair

To tell the story from shore to shore,
  From sea to sea, and from sun to sun.

Because, as I think I have said before,
    I like to see justice done.

So, whatever you've read or seen or heard,
    Believe me, good people, I tell the true
And only genuine—take my word—
    Story of little Boy Blue.

GREETING.

KIND friends, we welcome you to-day
    With songs of merry glee ;
Your loving smiles we strive to win,
    Each face we love to see.

Sweet welcomes then to one and all,
    And may your smiles approve;
And may we never miss the light
    Of faces that we love.

OBEYING ORDERS.

AN English farmer was one day at work in the fields, when he saw a party of huntsmen riding about his farm. He had one field that he was specially anxious they should not ride over, as the crop was in a condition to be badly injured by the tramp of horses ; so he sent a boy in his employ to this field, telling him to shut the gate and keep watch over it, and on no account to let it be opened. The boy went as he was bid ; but was scarcely at his post before the huntsmen rode up, and ordered the gate to be opened. The boy refused, saying he had received orders to keep the gate closed. Threats and bribes were offered in vain. After awhile one of the men advanced and said in stern tones : "My boy, do you know me ? I am the Duke of Wellington—and I *command* you to open the gate."

The boy lifted his cap, and said : "I am sure the Duke of Welling-

3—S C.

ton would not wish me to disobey orders.   I must keep this gate
shut; no one is to pass through without my master's permission."

  Greatly pleased, the sturdy old warrior lifted his own hat, and said:
" I honor the man or boy who can be neither bribed nor frightened
into doing wrong.   With an army of such soldiers, I could conquer
the world."

"THE PRETTIEST GIRL."

WE had such fun on Valentine's Day
    With the little girls who live over the way!
    Teddy and I, and Jed and Joe,
Picked out the prettiest girls, you know,
And wrote 'em things about "Violets blue,
And sugar is sweet, and so are you,"
And only that Bobby said it was mean,
I wanted to write, "The grass is green,
And so are you," and send it out
To a girl we fellers don't care about.

But Bobby he's queer, and doesn't go
For fun like the rest of us chaps, you know.
Why, who do you think he chose to be
His Valentine?   Now, if I'd been he,
I'd rather have chosen—never mind;
I'll tell you about it, and you will find
That if ever you want a feller that's queer,
You'll get him in Bobby, never you fear.

You see, we boys we had all picked out,
As I told you, the prettiest girls about.
But Bob he said there wasn't a girl
As pretty as his, and there wasn't a curl
On any girl's head that could half compare
With his chosen Valentine's soft, fine hair.
And he said her eyes were a whole lot bluer
Than any skies, and double the truer,

And that he was going to be her knight,
And take care of her always with main and might.

He wouldn't tell us his Valentine's name
Till the regular day for Valentines came,
And Mamma had hers, and Sister, you know,
(Of course from Papa, and Sister's beau).
Then Bob he told us to come ahead,
And he'd prove the truth of all he had said.
And where do you think he took us boys?
Hushing us up at the leastest noise,
And making us promise not to laugh,
Nor quiz him, nor give him any chaff?
Why, he opened Grandmamma's door. "See there!"
He said.
            It was Grandmamma, I declare!
Grandmamma sitting and knitting away:
Sweet Grandmamma, with her hair so gray,
Lying all soft on her forehead in curls
Just as pretty as any girl's.
And I never had noticed before how blue
Were Grandmamma's eyes. It was really true,
As Bobby had said, that there never were skies
One bit bluer than Grandmamma's eyes.

So she was his Valentine, he was her knight,
And somehow we all thought Bobby was right
When he kissed her hand, and cried, in glee,
"Dear Grandma's 'the prettiest girl,' you see;
Of course, I chose her instead of Mamma,
For she, you know, belongs to Papa.
But Grandpa's in heaven, and so I knew
That Grandma must be my Valentine true."

                                    MARY D. BRINE.

THE SQUIRREL'S LESSON.

TWO little squirrels, out in the sun,
    One gathered nuts and the other had none;
    "Time enough yet," his constant refrain;
"Summer is still only just on the wane."

Listen, my child, while I tell you his fate:
He roused him at last, but he roused him too late;
Down fell the snow from a pitiless cloud,
And gave little squirrel a spotless white shroud.

Two little boys in a schoolroom were placed,
One always perfect, the other disgraced;
"Time enough yet for my learning," he said;
"I will climb, by and by, from the foot to the head."

Listen, my darling; their locks are turned gray;
One as a Governor sitteth to-day;
The other, a pauper, looks out at the door
Of the almshouse, and idles his days as of yore

Two kinds of people we meet every day·
One is at work, the other at play,
Living uncared for, dying unknown—
The busiest hive hath ever a drone.

HATTIE'S VIEWS ON HOUSECLEANING.

OUR folks have been cleaning house—and, oh! it is just dread·
ful, I think! Why, a little girl might just as well have no
mamma as to have a mamma who is cleaning house. She
does not have any time to tend to me at all. She ties her head up in
an old apron, and wears an ugly old dress, and she don't look a bit
pretty. Then she pulls everything out of its place, and the house
looks—oh! so bad. We do not have any good dinners, either 'cause

there's no time to stop to get them ready. And I cannot find my dear Margaret that was broken a little, and the sawdust ran out of her. Mamma said she made so much dirt that she must be burnt up, and oh! I'm afraid that is where she has gone. And ever so many of my playthings are lost—lost in the housecleaning. What if they were old and broken! I loved them. So is it any wonder I think housecleaning is a dreadful thing?

When I grow up to be a big woman, I mean never to clean house at all, but be just as dirty and happy as I can. What's the world made of if it isn't made of dirt?

LITTLE DOT.

[The touching incident that gave rise to the following lines occurred in one of our large cities. Crouched upon the curbstone in a blinding snowstorm there was a little match-girl apparently not more than six years old. Attracted by her sobs, an old gentleman approached her and kindly asked, "Who are you, my little girl, that you are here in this storm?" Raising her large brown eyes, brimming with tears, she sobbed, "Oh, I'm only little Dot!"]

CROUCHING on the icy pavement,
  Sobbing, shivering with the cold,
Garments scant around her clinging,
  All her matches yet unsold;
Visions of a cheerless garret,
  Cruel blows not soon forgot,
While through choking sobs the murmur,
  "Oh, I'm only little Dot!"

Deeper than the icy crystals,
  Though their keenness made her start,
Is the hungry, aching longing
  In the little match-girl's heart.
No kind voice to cheer and comfort;
  Ah! by fortune quite forgot,
Who can wonder at the murmur,
  "Oh, I'm only little Dot!"

Far above the clouds and snowstorms,
Where the streets have pearly gates,
In that home a sainted mother,
For the little match-girl waits.
By the throng of waiting angels,
Little one you're ne'er forgot,
In the home of many mansions
There is room for little Dot.

DOT AND DOLLY.

SWEET little Dot on the doorstep sits, with Dolly wrapped in a
shawl,—
Her own thin dress is faded and patched, but Dolly has none at
all.
She kisses and cuddles her little pet in a way 'tis joy to see,
And whispers, "I know we's poor, but I's got you, and you's got me!"

Rocking her treasure to and fro, in the silent summer air,
Her chubby chin to her bosom went, and her hands forgot their care;
Her dimpled feet into dreamland slipped, just as upon the scene
A lady rode, with jewels and silk begirt like a very queen.

Her happy darling, just Dot's own size, the child and the dolly spied,
Then pointed, grasping her mamma's arm, to the half-wrapped pet,
and cried,
"Oh, mamma! look at her dolly—see! aren't you 'fraid it's catching
cold?
Please let me give it Rosa's dress, you know it's getting old."

She slipped from the carriage, and quick the work of the little maid
was done,
And Dot's poor Dolly was in a dress, the prettiest under the sun!
Gold and silver, satin and gauze, stockings, and bright blue shoes,
And money, as much in her pocket put as a doll in a year could use.

Then away, with a smile that almost laughed, so great was the giver's
    glee,
She went, with many a backward look, and said "I's afraid she'll see!
Hurry up Tom, mamma!" and quick away to their palace home they
    flew,
While Dot was dreaming a wonderful dream, of fairies and Dolly, too.

They had satin dresses and gauzy wings, all speckled with drops of
    gold ;
They danced in troops on the lilac leaves, and a leaf would a dozen
    hold ;
And Dolly was dancing with all her might, in the prettiest dress of all,
And spangled wings, when up sprang Dot, afraid lest her pet should
    fall.

She opened her eyes, and merrily laughed, in happiness and surprise,
As Dolly dressed in her fairy best, looked into her wondering eyes.
"Oh, mamma, what shall I do ?" cried Dot, in a comic tone of dismay,
"My Dolly has borrowed a fairy's clothes, and the fairies have runned
    away!

"I's afraid she's been naughty and stealed—but then I don't most
    think she would ;
I guess they did it o' purpose, cos my Dolly's so awful good!
You pitty, sweet girl! I'll let you wear 'em awhile, I guess, and then,
If they want 'em ever, we'll give 'em back, when the fairies come
    again !"

Well, that was a long, long time ago—sweet Dot is a woman grown,
And little ones gather to hear her tell a tale of her childhood flown ;
And many a story she tells at eve, but nicest of all she knows
Is the one that tells of Dot and her doll that borrowed the fairy's
    clothes.

MINNIE W. PATTERSON.

MATTIE'S WANTS AND WISHES

I WANTS a piece of cal'co
    To make my doll a dress.
I doesn't want a big piece;
    A yard'll do I guess.
I wish you 'fred my needle,
    And find my fimble, too—
I has such heaps o' sewin'
    I don't know what to do.

My Hepsy tored her apron
    A tum'lin down the stair,
And Cæsar's lost his pantnoons,
    And needs anozzer pair.
I wants my Maud a bonnet;
    She hasn't none at all;
And Fred must have a jacket;
    His ozzer one's too small.

I wants to go to grandma's;
    You promised me I might,
I know she'd like to see me;
    I wants to go to-night.
She lets me wipe the dishes,
    And see in grandpa's watch—
I wish I'd three, four pennies
    To buy some butter-scotch.

I wants some newer mittens—
    I wish you'd knit me some,
'Cause most my finger freezes,
    They leaks so in the fum,
I wored 'em out last summer,
    A pullin' George's sled;

THE COQUETTE'S ART

"WITH BEWITCHING GLANCE, AND GESTURES RARE,
SHE SOUGHT TO WIN THE HEARTS OF MEN."

THE SOLDIER-BOY

I wish you wouldn't laugh so—
   It hurts me in my head.

I wish I had a cookie;
   I'm hungry's I can be.
If you hasn't pretty large ones,
   You'd better bring me free.
I wish I had a p'ano—
   Won't you buy me one to keep?
O, dear! I feels so tired,
   I wants to go to sleep.   GRACE GORDON.

THE WHITE ROSE AND THE POPPY.

"DEAR me, you're so red!" cried the White Rose
   To the Poppy nodding near;
"I am sure you must feel most gaudy,
   And very conspicuous, dear;
I am dreadfully sorry for you,
   It is trying to be so bright.
One feels, and looks so modest
   When one's dress is perfectly white.

"To seem to solicit attention,
   Though it may not be all your fault,
Is contrary, quite, to the manners
   Which I have always been taught
Are becoming in a lady;
   And so, as I have said,
You have my heartfelt sympathy
   For being so terribly red."

Poor Poppy! Her blush grew deeper,
   And she hung her head, so bright,
And sighed, and trembled on her stem,
   And wished that she could have been white;

For to be called flaunting and gaudy,
  To be thought immodest and bold,
Made her petals quiver with anguish,
  And her very calyx grow cold.

But the comforting south wind kissed her,
  And the whispered words he said
Stilled the poor fluttering spirits;
  And she lifted her lovely head,
And turned with a dignity stately
  To her neighbor clad in white,
Saying, "I was made a red poppy,
  So surely was meant to be bright.

"There must be in this great garden,
  Room, and to spare for us all;
A place for the creeping myrtle,
  A place for the oak tree tall,
Room for each shade and color,
  And need for each plant and tree,
Need for the white and the lilac,
  And even the red, like me.
Ah! yes, the Lord of the garden
  Has placed us each in our bed;
You in your spotless white robe,
  I, in my garments red.

"You are not a red poppy,
  I am not a white rose;
But the Master and Lord of the garden
  Has work for each flower that grows—
Work for the high and the lowly,
  Work for the great and small,
Yea, the loving hand which planted
  Has need of us, one and all."   ANNIE L. HANNAH.

LITTLE BY LITTLE.

ONE step and then another, and the longest walk is ended;
　One stitch and then another, and the widest rent is mended;
One brick upon another, and the highest wall is made;
One flake upon another, and the deepest snow is laid.

Then do not frown nor murmur at the work you have to do,
Or say that such a mighty task you never can get through;
But just endeavor, day by day, another point to gain,
And soon the mountain that you feared will prove to be a plain.

THE FARMER.
[FOR SEVERAL BOYS.]

THIS is the way the happy farmer (1)
　Plows his piece of ground,
That from the little seeds he sows
　A large crop may abound.

This is the way he sows the seed, (2)
　Dropping with careful hand,
In all the furrows well prepared
　Upon the fertile land.

This is the way he cuts the grain (3)
　When bending with its weight;
And thus he bundles it in sheaves, (4)
　Working long and late.

And then the grain he threshes thus (5)
　And stores away to keep;
And thus he stands contentedly (6)
　And views the plenteous heap.

1. Arms extended forward as though holding a plow.
2. A motion as of taking seed out of a bag or basket, and scattering with the right hand.
3. Motion as of cutting with a scythe.
4. Arms curved and extended forward.
5. Hands as though grasping a flail. Strike with some force.
6. Erect position, arms folded, or hands on the hips.

A CHRISTMAS EVE ADVENTURE.

ONCE on a time, in a queer little town
    On the shore of the Zuyder Zee,
When all the good people were fast asleep
    A strange thing happened to me!

Alone, the night before Christmas,
    I sat by the glowing fire,
Watching the flame as it rose and fell,
    While the sparks shot high and higher.

Suddenly one of these sparks began
    To flicker and glimmer and wink
Like a big bright eye, till I hardly knew
    What to do or to say or to think.

Quick as a flash, it changed to a face,
    And what in the world did I see
But dear old Santa Claus nodding his head,
    And waving his hand to me!

"Oh! follow me, follow me!" soft he cried—
    And up through the chimney with him
I mounted, not daring to utter a word
    Till we stood on the chimney's rim.

"Now tell me, I beg you, dear Santa Claus,
    Where am I going with you?"
He laughingly answered, "Why don't you know
    To travel the wide world through!

"From my crystal palace, far in the North,
    I have come since dark—and see
These curious things for the little folk
    Who live on the Zuyder Zee."

Then seating himself in his reindeer sledge,
   And drawing me down by his side,
He whistled, and off on the wings of the wind
   We flew for our midnight ride.

But first, such comical presents he left
   For the little Dutch girls and boys,—
Onions and sausages, wooden-faced dolls,
   Cheeses and gingerbread toys!

Away we hurried far to the South,
   To the beautiful land of France;
And there we showered the loveliest gifts,—
   Flaxen-haired dolls that could dance,

Soldiers that marched at the word of command,
   Necklaces, bracelets, and rings,
Tiny gold watches, all studded with gems,
   And hundreds of exquisite things.

Crossing the Channel, we made a short call
   In Scotland and Ireland, too;
Left a warm greeting for England and Wales,
   Then over the ocean we flew

Straight to America, where by myself,
   Perched on a chimney high,
I watched him scramble and bustle about
   Between the earth and the sky.

Many a stocking he filled to the brim,
   And numberless Christmas trees
Burst into bloom at his magical touch!
   Then all of a sudden, a breeze

Caught us and bore us away to the South,
  And afterward blew us " out West ; "
And never till dawn peeped over the hills
  Did we stop for a moment's rest.

"Christmas is coming! " he whispered to me,
  "You can see his smile in the sky—
I wish Merry Christmas to all the world !
  My work is over—good-bye ! "

Like a flash he was gone, and I was alone—
  For all of this happened to me
Once on a time, in a queer little town
  On the shore of the Zuyder Zee !

DO YOUR DUTY.

DO your duty, little man,
  That's the way !
There's some duty in the plan
  Of every day.
Every day has some new task
  For your hand ;
Do it bravely—that's the way
  Life grows grand.

" Do your duty," says the sun
  High in heaven ;
To the dutiful, when tasks are done,
  Crowns are given :
Crowns of power and crowns of fame,
  Crowns of life :
In glory burns the victor's name,
  After strife.
Do your duty, never swerve—
  Smooth or rough—
Until God, whom we all serve,
  Says, " Enough."—LUELLA CLARK.

ROME WASN'T BUILT IN A DAY.

[FOR A BOY.]

THE boy who does a stroke and stops
　Will ne'er a great man be ;
'Tis the aggregate of single drops
　That makes the sea the sea.

The mountain was not at its birth
　A mountain, so to speak ;
The little atoms of sand and earth
　Have made its peak a peak.

Not all at once the morning streams,
　The gold above the gray ;
'Tis a thousand little yellow gleams
　That make the day the day.

Not from the snowdrifts May awakes
　In purples, reds, and greens ;
Spring's whole bright retinue it takes
　To make her queen of queens.

Upon the orchard rain must fall,
　And soak from branch to root ;
And blossoms bloom and fall withal,
　Before the fruit is fruit.

The farmer needs must sow and till
　And wait the wheaten bread,
Then cradle, thresh, and go to mill,
　Before the bread is bread.

Swift heels may get the early shout,
　But, spite of all the din.

It is the patient holding out
    That makes the winner win.

Make this your motto, then, at start—
    'Twill help to smooth the way;
And steady up both hand and heart—
    "Rome wasn't built in a day!"   ALICE CARY.

PRESENTATION SPEECH.

DEAR TEACHER :—I have been requested by the young persons of this school (or institution) to offer you a slight token of our affection and regard. I cannot tell you how delighted I am to be the means of conveying to you the expression of our united love. What we offer you is a poor symbol of our feelings, but we know you will receive it kindly, as a simple indication of the attachment which each one of us cherishes for you in our heart of hearts. You have made our lessons pleasant to us—so pleasant that it would be ungrateful to call them tasks.

We know that we have often tried your temper and forbearance, but you have dealt gently with us in our waywardness, teaching us, by example as well as precept, the advantages of magnanimity and self-control. We will never forget you. We shall look back to this school (or institution) in after life, not as a place of penance, but as a scene of mental enjoyment, where the paths of learning were strewn with flowers; and whenever memory recalls our school-days, our hearts will warm toward you as they do to-day. I have been requested by my schoolmates not to address you formally, but as a beloved and respected friend. In that light, dear teacher, we all regard you.

Please accept, with our little present, our earnest good wishes. May you always be as happy as you have endeavored to make your pupils, and may they—nothing better could be wished for them—be always as faithful to their duties to others as you have been in your duties to them.

WELCOME FOR SCHOOL ENTERTAINMENT.

DEAR friends, with joy we welcome you,
    We greet you, one and all;
    We thank you for your presence here,
Both great as well as small.
We know you've come to hear us speak,
And see us act our parts:
We'll try to do our very best,
With glad and willing hearts.
We hope you will be entertained,
We'll strive to please each one:
And when our evening's work is o'er,
We'll trust you'll say "Well done."
Again we bid you welcome here
With joy our hearts are beating:
Kind friends we're glad to see you all,
Accept our evening greeting.   IDA M. HEDRICH

BETTY LEE.

SWEET Betty Lee, the village lass,
    With laughter brimming o'er,
Leaned out, to see the deacon pass,
    Across the old Dutch door.

The deacon, riding slowly by,
    Upon a sheepskin sat,
And 'neath the glance of Betty's eye
    He doffed his old-time hat.

Betty was lithesome, young and fair;
    The deacon, stiff and grim;
The sunshine lingered in her hair,
    And made it gold to him.

4—S.C.

The mischief sparkled in her eyes
   And dimpled in her chin—
A token of unfeigned surprise
   To see him gazing in.

Her bright blue eyes were opened wide,
   As watching for her fate,
And in her hands she held with pride—
   And wiped—a china plate.

The old Dutch door was cut in two,
   With Betty leaning o'er
The lower half, with eyes of blue—
   The deacon saw the door.

It was a pretty sight, and led
   His pious thoughts abroad;
No wonder that the deacon had
   "A message from the Lord."

The deacon from his sheepskin seat
   Bent toward her, slowly o'er,
And, gazing in the blue eyes sweet,
   Reined up before the door.

" Betty," said Deacon Marvin, " dear
   Betty, I tell thee true,
The Lord himself hath sent me here
   That I may marry you."

The sweet blush mantled o'er her face
   And crept across her brow—
She bowed her head with girlish grace
   Before the deacon's vow.

An olden story 'twas to tell,
　It sealed our Betty's fate,
Her eyes upon the doorstep fell—
　As also did her plate.

The maid looked up—a single tear
　Shone in the midday sun—
Then answered him with words sincere:
　"The Lord!　His will be done!"

The deacon slowly jogged along,
　The sheepskin at his knee,
And all the world broke into song
　For pretty Betty Lee.

The dishes soon were finished up,
　And Betty shone with pride,
For every homely plate and cup
　By love was glorified.

And Deacon Marvin, as he gazed
　Upon the setting sun,
Still heard her words, as half amazed
　She said: "His will be done."

And dreamed perhaps—for deacons dream—
　Beside his kitchen fire,
He saw our Betty's blue eyes gleam,
　Filled with a fond desire.

And this is how the deacon sped
　Within the by-gone time,
And how it was he came to wed
　Sweet Betty Lee of Lyme.

E. Norman Gunnison.

THE REASON WHY.

"WHEN I was at the party,"
  Said Betty (aged just four),
"A little girl fell off her chair,
  Right down upon the floor;
And all the other little girls
  Began to laugh, but me—
I didn't laugh a single bit,"
  Said Betty, seriously.

"Why not?" her mother asked her,
  Full of delight to find
That Betty—bless her little heart!—
  Had been so sweetly kind.
"Why didn't *you* laugh, darling?
  Or don't you like to tell?"
"I didn't laugh," said Betty,
  "'Cause it was me that fell!"

SONG OF THE ALL-WOOL SHIRT.

MY father bought an undershirt
  Of bright and flaming red—
"All wool, I'm ready to assert,
  Fleece-dyed," the merchant said.
"Your size is thirty-eight, I think;
  A forty you should get,
Since all-wool goods are bound to shrink
  A trifle when they're wet."

That shirt two weeks my father wore—
  Two washings that was all—
From forty down to thirty-four
  It shrank like leaf in fall.

I wore it then a day or two,
　But when 'twas washed again,
My wife said " Now 'twill only do
　For little brother Ben.''

A fortnight Ben squeezed into it,
　At last he said it hurt,
We put it on our babe—the fit
　Was good as any shirt.
We ne'er shall wash it more while yet
　We see its flickering light,
For if again that shirt is wet,
　'Twill vanish from our sight.

THE CAT'S BATH.

AS pussy sat washing her face by the gate,
　A nice little dog came to have a good chat;
And after some talk about matters of state,
　Said, with a low bow, " My dear Mrs. Cat,
I really do hope you'll not think I am rude;
　I am curious, I know, and that you may say—
Perhaps you'll be angry—but no, you're too good—
　Pray, why do you wash in that very odd way?
Now I every day rush away to the lake,
　And in the clear water I dive and I swim;
I dry my wet fur with a run and a shake,
　And am fresh as a rose and neat as a pin.

" But you any day in the sun may be seen,
　Just rubbing yourself with your red little tongue;
I admire the grace with which it is done—
　But really, now, are you sure you get yourself clean?"
The cat, who sat swelling with rage and surprise
　At this, could no longer her fury contain,

For she had always supposed herself rather precise,
And of her sleek neatness had been somewhat vain;
So she flew at poor doggy and boxed both his ears,
Scratched his nose and his eyes, and spit in his face,
And sent him off yelping; from which it appears
Those who ask prying questions may meet with disgrace.

THE LITTLE LIGHT.

The figures in this recitation refer to the corresponding numbers under typical
gestures in the first part of this volume.]

THE light[2] shone dim on the headland,
   For the storm was raging high;
I[24] shaded my eyes from the inner glare,
   And gazed on the west, gray sky.
It was dark and lowering; on the sea
   The waves were booming loud,
And the snow and the piercing winter sleet
   [23]Wove over all a shroud.

"God[21] pity the men on the sea to-night!"
   I said to my little ones,
And we shuddered as we heard afar
   The sound of minute-guns.
My good man came in, in his fishing coat,
   (He was wet and cold that night),
And he said[19]: "There'll lots of ship go down
   On the headland rocks to-night."

"Let the lamp burn all night, mother,"
   Cried little Mary then;
"'Tis but a little light, but still
   It might save drowning men."
"Oh! nonsense!" cried her father (he
   Was tired and cross that night),

"The headland lighthouse is enough."
    And he put out the light.

That night[9], on the rocks below us,
    A noble ship went down,
But one was saved from the ghastly wreck,
    The rest were left to drown.
"We steered by a little light," he said,
    " Till we saw it sink from view;
If they'd only 'a left that light all night
    My mates might have been here, too!"[25]

Then little[27] Mary sobbed aloud;
    Her father blushed for shame;
" 'Twas our light that you saw," he said
    "And I'm the one to blame."
'Twas a little light—how small a thing!
    And trifling was its cost,
Yet for want of it a ship went down,
    And[19] a hundred souls were lost.

A BABY'S REFLECTIONS.

I 'M a very little baby,
    Little face and hands and feet;
And my mother says she never
    Saw a baby half so sweet.
It is nice to hear them talking
    In that way, but I can see,
Oh, a lot of little babies,
    Who all look and laugh like me.

When I look out of the window
    There's a baby in the glass,
And he waves his hands as I do
    To the people as they pass;

When I put out hands to touch him
   And to pat him on the cheek,
He will look and act as I do,
   But he'll never, never speak.

There's a baby in the mirror,
   There's a baby in the spoon,
And there's one in front of mother
   When we play a little tune.
These are very funny babies,
   Where I go they always come,
But I never hear them talking,
   So I guess they are deaf and dumb.

AMBITION.

LET us rise to higher heights :
   We can greater be than now ;
Spread our wings for longer flights
   Reach the mountain's topmost heights.

Better far to strive and die,
   Than never strive at all ;
Put all useless longings by,
   Hang the garland on the wall ;

Lay aside the lute and palm,
   Seize the stave and pilgrim staff ;
Free thee from delusive calm,
   Do no noble work by half.

Let us climb to lofty peaks,
   Dare the eaglet in its nest ;
Fortune crowns the soul who seeks ;
   Only failure sighs for rest.

THE LIGHT IN THE WINDOW.

"WILL Santa Claus come to-night, mother?" asked little Steenie, drawing his stool close to his mother's chair, and resting his curly head on her knee. The mother's face was very sad, as she stooped over and kissed the bright eyes upturned to hers.

"And if he does not, Steenie, little man, can we not wait till next Christmas? You know how the snow has drifted on the plain, and hidden the road; you know how dark it is now; he may not come to-night, dear."

"Come here to the window, Steenie," said Ev, who stood flattening his nose against the cold pane.

The two boys peered out into the darkness, where even the white snow which was piled and drifted in the yard and against the fences of the corrals was now hidden.

"Steenie," said Ev, so low that mother, sitting by the fire darning their little socks, the big tears rolling down her cheeks and dropping upon her work, and father, who was so ill and now lay asleep on the bed in the corner, could not hear, "Steenie," he said, his child's heart feeling heavy and sad, but his manly bravery prompting him to comfort his little brother in his sorrow, "see how dark it is out there; we can't even see the haystacks, nor the barn, nor nothing. If Santa Claus tried to come to-night he might get lost, and all his reindeer, and his sleigh, and his books, and his toys, and his goodies, and—and —everything. And if I was you I'd er heap ruther he wouldn't try to come to-night—wouldn't you, Steenie?—than for him to get lost on the prairie. Don't cry, Steenie! Mother will hear you, and it will make her sad, too, and father might wake up. Don't cry; try to be a man, like mother said, and Santa Claus won't forget us when it aint so dark and he can get here."

The brave little fellows both tried very hard to keep back the tears, but somehow they just would come, and by-and-by, when mother called to them to go to bed, they were very wet little faces that were held up to hers for a kiss.

"May I hang up our stockings and pray to God to make it light, so Santa Claus can see how to come, mother?" said Steenie.

"Yes, dear," said mother.

She tucked the covers well about the boys when they pressed their tearful faces upon the pillows, and the little fellows lay very still for some time.

"Ev," said Steenie, by-and-by, when mother's light was out and he knew she was gone to bed, too; "do you think Santa Claus could see if there was a light?"

"He might," said Ev, drowsily.

Steenie turned over, stuck his head out from under the cover and opened his eyes very wide to keep from going to sleep. He had not many minutes to wait before Ev's regular breathing told that he was asleep. It was very dark and Steenie could not see a wink, but he reached down to the foot of the bed, and got Ev's overcoat and slipped into it. It was not much too big for him, but it was getting very tight on Ev.

"Now I shall not take cold," he said, as he felt for the matches which mother always put on tne little table so Ev could make a light if Steenie had the croup. "Yes, here they are," said Steenie to himself, "and I know the lantern is hanging just above the bed on the peg by the window, for I saw Ev put it there."

It was but the work of a moment for him to strike a match and light the big lantern that hung near the bedpost. He saw the light spring up and shine through the bare window out into the white yard, over the white fence, across the white prairie beyond.

"If Santa Claus is coming that way he'll see my light," the little fellow said, as he crept back to bed; and very soon he was asleep. Steenie saw the light shine across the white yard and the white fence and the white prairie, but he did not see the poor, miserable little peddler, who struggled to his feet again when the bright gleam reached him, and who made another effort to get out of the drift by the roadside.

Steenie did not hear the faint knock at the door, as, almost frozen and well-nigh bent to the ground by the weight of his heavy pack, the peddler sank exhausted upon the steps. But mother heard, and let the poor man in, and the next morning the boys saw him.

And they saw something else, too. When they opened their eyes they saw the lantern still burning and the light of a beautiful Christmas day shining in upon their bright faces. And what were those piles of bundles upon the two chairs where Steenie had hung the stockings?

Out of bed the boys sprang, laughing and shouting to find their stockings stuffed with the candies they had longed for, round and flat and red and white. There were a new overcoat, new boots, new mittens for Ev and a new suit for Steenie, with a belt to buckle around his waist; there were books and pictures and everything they had wished for, down to Ev's jackknife and Steenie's ball.

"God answered my prayer, didn't he, mother?" said Steenie, joyfully.

PATIENCE ORIEL.

BE IN TIME.

E in time for every call;
    If you can't be first of all,
        Be in time.
If your teachers only find
You are never once behind,
But are, like the dial, true,
They will always trust in you:
        Be in time.

Never linger ere you start;
Set out with a willing heart;
        Be in time.
In the morning, up and on,
First to work, and soonest done:
This is how the goal's attained:
This is how the prize is gained:
        Be in time.

Those who aim at something great
Never yet were found too late:
    Be in time.
Life with all is but a school:
We must work with plan and rule,
With some noble end in view,
Ever steady, earnest, true:
    Be in time.

Listen, then, to wisdom's call—
Knowledge now is free to all:
    Be in time.
Youth must daily toil and strive,
Treasure for the future hive;
For the work they have to do,
Keep this motto still in view:
    Be in time.

HOW HIS GARMENTS GOT TURNED.

WHEN the golden sunlight dances on the bosom of the stream,
    And the silver lilies, starlike, 'mong the olive sedges gleam,
    When the bullfrog seeks the cover of the grasses tall and
        rank,
And the pickerel at noonday seeks the shadow of the bank,
Then the small boy goes in swimming in the costume of the mode
That was worn by fair Godiva when through Coventry she rode.

He splashes in the limpid stream with many a gleeful shout,
And to the bank returning puts his shirt on inside out;
And when his mother questions him, "How came that garment so?"
He looks upon it with surprise, and says he doesn't know;
When further pressed to give the cause, this reason he employs:
"I must have turned a somersault when playing with the boys."

WHEN MAMMA WAS A LITTLE GIRL

WHEN mamma was a little girl
  (Or so they say to me)
She never used to romp or run,
Nor shout and scream with noisy fun,
  Nor climb an apple tree.
She always kept her hair in curl—
When mamma was a little girl.

When mamma was a little girl
  (It seems to her, you see)
She never used to tumble down,
Nor break her doll, nor tear her gown,
  Nor drink her papa's tea.
She learned to knit, "plain," "seam," and "purl"—
When mamma was a little girl.

But grandma says—it must be true—
  "How fast the seasons o'er us whirl!
Your mamma, dear, was just like you,
  When she was grandma's little girl."

THE TWO BROTHERS.

FROM THE TALMUD.

IN Palestine long years ago—
  So runs the legend old—
Where Kedron's sparkling waters flow
  Across their sands of gold,
And Mt. Moriah lifts his head
  Above the sunny plain,
Two brothers owned—as one—'tis said,
  A field of golden grain.

And when the autumn days had come
  And all the shocks and sheaves
Stood waiting for the "harvest home,"
  Among the withering leaves,
The elder brother said one night,
  "I'm stronger far than Saul,
My younger brother, 'tis but right
  That I should give him all
These sheaves that grow upon the plain
  We own together, so
I'll put with his my stacks of grain,
  And he will never know."

Scarce had he left the sheaves of wheat
  When quietly there came
Across the field with stealthy feet,
  And errand just the same—
The younger lad who said, "I see
  My brother Simon's need
Is greater far than mine, for he
  Hath wife and child to feed;
And so to him I'll give my sheaves,
  It is but right, I know—
And he will never think who leaves
  These wheat stacks on his row!"

Next morning when the brothers twain
  Began to count their store,
Behold! each found his stacks of grain
  To number as before!
"Why! how is this?" in great surprise
  Each to himself then said—
"I'll watch to-night and see who tries
  These tricks when I'm abed!"

And so, half way across the plain
    They met—each one bent o'er
With shocks and sheaves of golden grain
    To swell his brother's store!

Good Saul and Simon!   Would to-day
    More brothers might be found
Who seek each other's good alway,
    And in kind deeds abound.

THE PECULIAR NEIGHBOR.

"HE is so very peculiar,"
    His neighbors said with a smile,
" He works in the quarry yonder,
    The distance of half a mile.
He never complains or grumbles,
    But labors till close of day.
He is old and wretched and friendless,
    And very peculiar, they say."

That was all.   He was very "peculiar,"
    I found of the village folk,
And lived in a little cottage alone,
    'Neath the shade of a sheltering oak,
In the midst of a tiny garden patch,
    Just back from the noisy street.
But the heart that throbbed 'neath his ragged coat
    Was as noble a heart as beat.

Yes, he was truly " peculiar,"
    I heard, with a wondering start,
Of the kindly deeds that were daily done
    By that good, old-fashioned heart.

His coat, so ragged and worn with time,
   A brother might freely share:
Contented he with only a smile
   And a fervently whispered prayer.

When evening came, and he sat alone
   In his vine-wreathed doorway low,
Who cared if his lonely heart grew sad?
   His bitterness who should know?
And when he brushed, with his aged hand,
   The dew from his eyes so dim,
What mattered it if he pondered o'er
   The days that were sweet to him?

But then, when the sun in the heavens rose,
   He was up again with a smile,
Trudging along, in his shabby clothes,
   The distance of half a mile.
While the children clung to his sunburnt hands
   As he went on his cherry way;
And I wished to God, as I saw him pass,
   That more were " peculiar " to-day.

              HARRIET M. SPAULDING.

THE DEAD DOLL.

YOU needn't be trying to comfort me,
   I tell you my dolly is dead!
There's no use in saying she isn't
   With a crack like *that* in her head.
It's just like you said it wouldn't hurt
   Much to have my tooth out that day.
And then when the man most pulled my
   Head off you hadn't a word to say.

And I guess you must think I'm a baby
  When you say you can mend it with glue!
As if I didn't know better than that,
  Why just suppose it were you!
You might make her *look* all mended;
  But what do I care for looks,
Why, glue's for chairs, and tables,
  And toys and the backs of books.

My dolly, my own little daughter!
  Oh, but it's the awfullest crack!
It just makes me sick to think
  Of the sound, when her poor head went whack
Against that horrible brass thing
  That holds up the little shelf.
Now, nursey, what makes you remind me?
  I know that I did it myself.

I think you must be crazy,
  You'd get her another head?
What good would forty heads do her?
  I tell you my dolly is dead!
And to think I hadn't quite finished
  Her elegant new spring hat,
And I took a sweet ribbon of hers
  To tie on that horrid cat!

When my mama gave me that ribbon,
  I was playing out in the yard.
She said to me most expressly,
  "Here's a ribbon for Hildegarde."
And I went and put it on Tabby,
  And Hildegarde saw me do it.
But I said to myself, "O never mind,
  I don't believe she knew it."

5—S.C

But I know she knew it now,
    And I just believe, I do,
That her poor little heart was broken,
    And so her head broke, too ;
Oh, my baby, my little baby,
    I wish my head had been hit,
For I've hit it over and over,
    And it wasn't cracked a bit.

But since the darling is dead
    She'll want to be buried, of course
We will take my little wagon, nurse,
    And you shall be the horse.
And I'll walk behind and cry,
    And we'll put her in this, you see,
This dear little box, and we'll bury
    Her then under the maple tree.

And papa will make me a tombstone
    Like the one he made for my bird,
And he'll put what I tell him on it,
    Yes, every single word.
I shall say, " Here lies Hildegarde,
    A beautiful doll who is dead.
She died of a broken heart
    And a dreadful crack in her head."

BRAVE AND TRUE.

WHATEVER you are, be brave, boys!
    The liar's a coward and slave, boys!
        Though clever at ruses,
        And sharp at excuses,
He's a sneaking and pitiful knave, boys!

Whatever you are, be frank, boys!
'Tis better than money and rank, boys;
  Still cleave to the right,
  Be lovers of light,
Be open, above board, and frank, boys!

Whatever you are, be kind, boys!
Be gentle in manner and mind, boys;
  The man gentle in mien,
  Words, and temper, I ween,
Is the gentleman truly refined, boys!

But, whatever you are, be true, boys!
Be visible through and through, boys!
  Leave to others the shamming,
  The "greening" and "cramming,"
In fun and in earnest, be true, boys!

                              HENRY DOWNTON.

MAKE CHILDHOOD SWEET.

WAIT not till the little hands are at rest
  Ere you fill them full of flowers;
Wait not for the crowning tuberose
  To make sweet the last sad hours;
But while in the busy household land,
Your darlings still need your guiding hand,
  Oh, fill their lives with sweetness!

Wait not 'till the little hearts are still,
  For the loving look and phrase;
But while you gently chide a fault
  The good deed kindly praise.
The word you would speak beside the cier
Falls sweeter far on the living ear;
  Oh! fill young lives with sweetness!

Ah! what are kisses on clay cold lips
  To the rosy mouth we press,
When our wee one flees to her mother's arms,
  For love's tenderest caress?
Let never a worldly bauble keep
Your heart from the joy each day should reap,
  Circling young lives with sweetness.

Give thanks each morn for the sturdy boys,
  Give thanks for the fairy girls;
With a dower of wealth like this at home,
  Would you rifle the earth for pearls?
Wait not for death to gem love's crown,
But daily shower life's blessings down,
  And fill young hearts with sweetness.

THE CHICKENS.

SAID the first little chicken,
  With a queer little squirm,
"I wish I could find
  A fat little worm."

Said the next little chicken,
  With an odd little shrug,
"I wish I could find
  A fat little slug."

Said the third little chicken,
  With a sharp little squeal,
"I wish I could find
  Some nice yellow meal."

Said the fourth little chicken,
  With a small sigh of grief,
"I wish I could find
  A little green leaf."

Said the fifth little chicken,
  With a faint little moan,
"I wish I could find
  A wee gravel stone."

"Now, see here," said the mother
  From the green garden patch,
"If you want any breakfast,
  Just come here and scratch."

WHOSE GIRL?

WELL, whose girl am I, anyway?
  I fell down cellar yesterday
  And gave my head an awful bump.
If you could only see the lump!
Mamma called me when I cried,
And hugged me close up to her side,
And said, "I'll kiss and make it well,
Mamma's own girl, how hard she fell!"

When papa took me out to play
Where all the men were raking hay,
He put me on old Dobbin's back;
And when they gave the whip a crack
Off he threw me. Papa said,
When I got up and rubbed my head,
And shut my lips and winked my eyes,
"Papa's brave girl, she never cries."

And when to grandmama's I go—
Well, you would be surprised to know
Of all the pies and cakes so sweet,
And jams and tarts she makes to eat,

And tells me eat my fill, for more
There is to spare—a goodly store—
Saved up for me, her precious pearl—
I am, she says, " grandmama's girl."

And grandpa says : " I'll buy her soon
A little pony of her own.
She'll learn to ride it well, I know,
Because she's grandpa's girl, ho! ho!"
And plenty other people say,
" Well! how are you, my girl, to-day ?"
Now can you tell me, if you try,
How many little girls am I?

THE LITTLE BOY'S LAMENT.

OH! why must I always be washed so clean
And scrubbed and drenched for Sunday,
When you know, very well, for you've always seen,
That I'm dirty again on Monday?

My hair is filled with the lathery soap,
Which adown my ears is dripping;
And my smarting eyes I can scarcely ope,
And my lips the suds are sipping.

It's down my neck and up my nose,
And to choke me you seem to be trying;
That I'll shut my mouth you need not suppose,
For how can I keep from crying?

You rub as hard as ever you can,
And your hands are hard, to my sorrow;
No woman shall wash me when I am a man,
And I wish I was one to-morrow.

LOST TOMMY.

PRAY, have you seen our Tommy?
   He's the cutest little fellow,
With cheeks as round as apples,
   And hair the softest yellow.
You see, 'twas quite a while ago,—
   An hour or two, perhaps,—
When grandma sent him off to buy
   A pound of ginger-snaps.

We have traced him to the baker's,
   And part way back again;
We found a little paper sack
   Lying empty in the lane.
But Tommy and the ginger-snaps
   Are missing totally;
I hope they both will reappear
   In time enough for tea.

We have climbed up to the garret,
   And scoured the cellar through;
We have ransacked every closet,
   And the barn and orchard too;
We have hunted through the kitchen,
   And the pantry? Oh! of course,—
We have screamed and shouted "Tommy"
   Until we're fairly hoarse.

Ah! here's the laundry basket,
   Within I'll take a peep.
Why—what is this curled up so tight?
   'Tis Tommy, fast asleep.
O mamma, auntie, grandma!
   Come and see the fun.

Tommy, where's the ginger-snaps?
　"Eaten!—every one!"

"Bless my heart!" laughs auntie,
　"Dear, dear, I shall collapse;
Where could he stow them all away?
　A pound of ginger-snaps?"

But mamma falls to kissing,
　Forgetting fright and toil,
While grandma bustles out to fetch
　A dose of castor oil.　Mrs. Julia M. Dana.

NEVER SAY FAIL.

IN life's rosy morning,
　In manhood's pride,
Let this be your motto,
　Your footsteps to guide:
In storms and in sunshine,
　Whatever assail,
We'll onward and conquer,
　And never say fail.

GRANDPAPA'S SPECTACLES.

GRANDPAPA'S spectacles cannot be found!
　He has searched all the rooms, high and low, round and round
Now he calls to the young ones, and what does he say!
"Ten cents to the child who will find them to-day."

Then Harry and Nelly and Edward all ran,
And a most thorough search for the glasses began.
And dear little Nell in her generous way
　Said, "I'll look for them, Grandpa, without any pay."
15 S. S. S.

All through the big Bible she searched with care,
It lies on the table by Grandpapa's chair.
They feel in his pockets, they peep in his hat,
They pull out the sofa and shake out the mat.

Then down on the floor, like good-natured bears,
Go Harry and Ned under tables and chairs,
Till quite out of breath, Ned is heard to declare,
He believed that those glasses are not anywhere.

But Nelly, who, leaning on Grandpapa's knee,
Was thinking most earnestly, "where can they be?"
Looked suddenly up in the kind, faded eyes,
And her own shining brown ones grew big with surprise.

She clapped with her hands, all her dimples came out,
She turned to the boys with a bright, roguish shout,
"You may leave off your looking, both Harry and Ned,
For there are the glasses on Grandpapa's head."

THE STOLEN CUSTARD.

SUGAR-TOOTHED Dick
   For dainties was sick,
So he slowly stole into the kitchen,
Snatched a cup from the pantry,
   And darted out quick,
Unnoticed by mother or Gretchen.

   Whispered he, "There's no cake,
   For to-morrow they bake,
But this custard looks rich and delicious;
   How they'll scold at the rats,
   Or the mice, or the cats;
For of me I don't think they're suspicious.

" They might have filled up
Such a mean little cup!
And for want of a spoon I must drink it :
But 'tis easy to pour—
Hark! who's at the door?"
And the custard went down ere you'd think it.

With a shriek he sprang up;
To the floor dashed the cup;
Then he howled, tumbled, sputtered, and blustered
Till the horrible din
Brought the whole household in—
He had swallowed a cupful of mustard!

THE BEGGAR BABY.

PALE and weary, strangely old,
Wan with hunger, pinched with cold,
Clothed with rags, around it rolled—
A little beggar baby.

Careless travellers going by,
Walked around, lest, coming nigh,
They might hear the hungry cry
Of the poor beggar baby.

Rich men passed, and thought within,
"'Twere well that life had never been,"
As though misfortune were a sin
In a poor beggar baby.

Only the pauper mother smiled,
Only the mother blessed the child,
And murmured love in accents mild
To that poor beggar baby.

But by and by the baby died,
And they buried it on the paupers' side
Of the yard ;—only the mother cried
    For that poor beggar baby.

But lo ! beyond the pauper tomb
A wondrous light stole through the gloom,
And voices sang, "In heaven there's room
    For that poor beggar baby."

And then in garments white and new,
Upward the ranks of angels through,
The radiant ransomed spirit flew
    Of that poor beggar baby.

A LITTLE BOY'S TROUBLES.

I THOUGHT when I'd learned my letters
    That all of my troubles were done ;
But I find myself much mistaken—
    They only have just begun.
Learning to read was awful,
    But nothing like learning to write ;
I'd be sorry to have you tell it,
    But my copy-book is a sight !

The ink gets over my fingers ;
    The pen cuts all sorts of shines,
And won't do at all as I bid it ;
    The letters won't stay on the lines,
But go up and down and all over,
    As though they were dancing a jig—
They are there in all shapes and sizes,
    Medium, little, and big.

The tails of the g's are so contrary,
　　The handles get on the wrong side
Of the d's, and the k's, and the h's,
　　Though I've certainly tried and tried
To make them just right; it is dreadful,
　　I really don't know what to do,
I'm getting almost distracted—
　　My teacher says she is too.

My teacher says, little by little
　　To the mountain tops we climb;
It isn't all done in a minute,
　　But only a step at a time;
She says that all the scholars,
　　All the wise and learned men,
Had each to begin as I do;
　　If that's so, where's my pen?   CARLOTTA PERRY.

"GIVE THE YOUNGSTERS A CHANCE."

OH! here we are! don't leave us out,
　　Just because we're little boys!
Though we're not so old and stout,
　　In the world we make a noise!
You're a year or two ahead,
　　But we step by step advance;
All the world's before you spread—
　　Give us smaller boys a chance!

Never slight us in your play,
　　You were once as small as we;
We'll be big, like you, some day,
　　Then, perhaps, our power you'll see.
We will meet you, when we're grown.
　　With a brave and fearless glance;

Don't think all this world's your own—
    Give us little lads a chance!

Little hands will soon be strong
    For the work that they must do ;
Little lips will sing their song
    When these early days are through.
So, you big boys, if we're small,
    On our toes you needn't dance;
There is room enough for all,
    Give the younger boys a chance!

"DON'T GIVE UP THE SHIP."

YOU'RE on the sea of life, boys,
    Your ship is staunch and strong ;
You're sailing smoothly now, boys,
    But storms will come ere long.
Then boldly furl your sail, boys,
    And let the tempest " rip,"
Stand bravely by the helm, boys,
    And " Don't give up the ship! "

Though clouds o'ercast the sky, boys,
    The sun is bright behind ;
And though the waves roll high, boys,
    They'll soon calm down, you'll find.
So always keep up heart, boys,
    With cheerful eye and lip ;
And let your watchword e'er, boys,
    Be, "Don't give up the ship! "

Beyond the raging sea, boys,
    You'll find at last a rest,
If only on your trip, boys,
    You do your " level best."

There waits for each a crown, boys,
  So take a manly grip;
There waits for all eternal life
  Who "Don't give up the ship."

                                HESTER HUNT.

LITTLE EFFORTS.

A LITTLE child I am indeed,
    And little do I know;
Much help and care I yet shall need,
    That I may wiser grow,
If I would ever hope to do
    Things great and good and useful too.

But even now I ought to try
    To do what good I may;
God never meant that such as I
    Should only live to play,
And talk and laugh, and eat and drink,
    And sleep and wake, and never think.

One gentle word that I may speak,
    Or one kind, loving deed,
May, though a trifle, poor and weak,
    Prove like a tiny seed;
And who can tell what good may spring
    From such a very little thing.

Then let me try each day and hour,
    To act upon this plan;
What little good is in my power;
    To do it while I can.
If to be useful thus I try,
    I may do better by and by.

DEWDROPS.

THE dewdrops on the summer morn
    Sparkle on the grass ;
The village children brush them off
    As through the fields they pass.
There are no gems in monarch's crown
    More beautiful than they,
And yet we scarcely notice them,
    But tread them off in play.

MICE.

THEY break the kitchen windows
    And overturn the chairs ;
They cut the doors and tables—
    Much wicked work is theirs.
Your watch they often handle,
    And sometimes let it fall ;
Which fact is quite surprising
    When told of rodents small.

They hide your books and papers,
    Unlock the doors and gates ;
They revel in the pantry
    And rattle down the plates.
They fill your boots with pebbles,
    And to your great dismay,
A garret full of pussies
    Can't keep the knaves away.

But mice don't slam the shutters,
    And sail your hats for boats,
And give away to beggars
    Your pantaloons and coats.

At last, you muse on Darwin,
  And, much to your annoy,
You find those mice developed
  Into the youngest boy.

HOE OUT YOUR ROW.

ONE day, a lazy farmer's boy,
  Was hoeing out the corn,
And moodily had listened long
  To hear the dinner horn.
The welcome blast was heard at last,
  And down he dropped his hoe;
But the good man shouted in his ear,
  " My boy, hoe out your row."

Although a "hard one" was the row,
  To use a ploughman's phrase,
And the lad, as sailors have it,
  Beginning well to " haze,"
" I can," he said, and manfully
  He seized again his hoe
And the good man smiled to see
  The boy " hoe out his row."

The lad that text remembered long,
  And proved the moral well,
That perseverance to the end
  At last will nobly tell.
Take courage, man! resolve you can,
  And strike a vigorous blow;
In life's great field of varied toil,
  Always "hoe out your row."

VIRGINIA HARNED AS "TRILBY."

THE GODDESS OF LIBERTY
(Suggestion for Tableau)

ENCORES.

A STORY OF CHINESE LOVE.

THE festive Ah Goo
    And Too Hay, the fair—
They met and the two
    Concluded to pair.

They "spooned" in the way
    That most lovers do,
And Ah Goo kissed Too Hay,
    And Too Hay kissed Ah Goo.

Said the festive Ah Goo,
    As his heart swelled with pride,
"Me heap likee you—
    You heap be my blide."

And she, looking down,
    All so modest and pretty,
'Twixt a smile and a frown,
    Gently murmured, "You betee."

AN INQUIRING FRIEND.

A GENTLEMAN riding in an Eastern railway car, which was rather sparsely supplied with passengers, observed in a seat before him a lean, slab-sided Yankee, every feature of whose face seemed to ask a question, and a circumstance soon proved that he had a more "inquiring mind." Before him, occupying the entire seat, sat a lady in deep black; and after shifting his position several times, and manœuvring to get an opportunity to look into her face, he at length caught her eye.

6—S.C.

"In affliction?" "Yes," responded the lady. "Parent—father or mother?" "No, sir." "Child, perhaps—boy or girl?" "No, sir; not a child—I have no children." "Husband, then, I expect?" "Yes," was the curt answer. "Hum! cholera?—a tradin' man, maybe?" "My husband was a sea-faring man—the captain of a vessel—he didn't die of cholera; he was drowned." "Oh, drowned, eh?" pursued the inquisitor, hesitating for a brief instant—"Save his *chist?*" "Yes; the vessel was saved, and my husband's effects," said the widow. "*Was* they?" asked the Yankee, his eyes brightening up—"*Pious* man?" "He was a member of the Methodist Church." The next question was a little delayed, but it came— "Don't you think you have great cause to be thankful that he was a pious man and saved his chist?" "I do," said the widow, abruptly, and turned her head to look out of the window.

The indefatigable "pump" changed his position, held the widow by his glittering eye once more, and propounded one more query, in a little lower tone, with his head a little inclined forward, over the back of the seat—"Was you calculating to get married again?" "Sir," said the widow, indignantly, "you are impertinent!" And she left her seat, and took another seat on the other side of the car. "'Pears to be a little huffy!" said the ineffable bore, turning to the man behind him. "What did they make you pay for that umbrella you've got in your hand?"

ARABELLA AND SALLY ANN.

ARABELLA was a schoolgirl,
  So was Sally Ann.
Hasty pudding can't be thicker
  Than two school-girls can.

These were thick as schoolgirls can be,
  Deathless love they swore,
Vowed that naught on earth should part them,—
  One forever more.

They grew up as schoolgirls will do,
   Went to parties, too,
And as oft before has happened,
   Suitors came to woo.

But as fate or luck would have it,
   One misguided man
Favored blue-eyed Arabella
   More than Sally Ann.

And, of course, it made no difference
   That the laws are such
That he could not wed two women,
   Though they wished it much.

So a coolness rose between them,
   And the cause,—a man.
Cold was Arabella—very;
   Colder Sally Ann.

Now they call each other "creature;"
   What is still more sad,—
Bella, though she won the treasure,
   Wishes Sally had.   PAUL CARSON.

REMARKABLE LONGEVITY.

A LADY declared that she never could see
   How the men could all smoke.—"Why, it kills them," said she
"I don't know," said Sam—"there's my father—ain't slow—
Who smokes every day, and he's eighty, you know."
"But, sir, if he never had used the vile weed,
He might have been ninety—he might, sir, indeed."

WET AND DRY.

ONE Sunday morn good parson Jones,
    Before the service hour,
While going from his home to church,
    Was troubled by a shower.

The lightning crinkled overhead,
    While peal on peal revolved;
The parson was a well-soaked man,
    And yet was not dissolved.

"I cannot preach," said parson Jones,
    "Without I feel the pain
Of being wet from crown to heel—
    Completely drenched with rain."

"You must go on," says deacon Smith
    With voice a little gruff,
"Though as a *man* you may be wet,
    As *preacher*, dry enough."   CLARK JILLSON.

A DISTURBED REVERIE.

LYING supine on the soft, matted grasses,
    Gazing up lazily into the blue
Of the sky, when the wandering wind as it passes
    Opens the branches for me to look through,

Idly I ponder, and ponder, and ponder,
    Thinking of nothing, yet happy and free;
Careless of everything, idly I wonder
    At the immensity opened to me.

Looking up listlessly, thoughtlessly dreaming,
    Mind a vacuity, life full of joy,
All the dull world seems with happiness teeming,
    With nothing to worry, or fret, or annoy.

Earth seem a paradise.   Why should I trouble
   Or toil to win heaven?   Why heaven is here!
Fortune is worthless, and fame but a bubble:
   I scorn them both, looking into the clear
Deep blue of the sky while the wild bees are humming,
   Above and around me, in harmony deep,
And over the meadows the breezes are coming
   To fan me, and soothe me, and lull me to sleep.

This, this is happiness, perfect, unmeasured;
   Long shall this day, without blemish or fleck
Stay in my memory, lovingly treasured—
   GREAT SCOTT! *There's a wasp down the back of my neck!*

A QUESTION.

AS Annie was carrying the baby one day,
   Tossing aloft the lump of inanity—
Dear to its father and mother no doubt,
   To the rest of the world a mere lump of humanity—
Sam came along, and was thinking then, maybe,
Full as much of Annie as she of the baby.

"Just look at the baby!" cried Ann, in a flutter,
   Giving its locks round her fingers a twirl:
'If I was a man I know that I couldn't
   Be keeping my hands off a dear little girl."
And Sam gave a wink, as if to say "Maybe,
Of the girls, I'd rather hug you than the baby!"

"Now kiss it!" she cried, still hugging it closer,
   "Its mouth's like the roses the honey-bee sips!"
Sam stooped to obey; and, as heads came together,
   There chanced to arise a confusion of lips!
And, as it occurred, it might have been, maybe,
That each got a kiss—Sam, Ann, and the baby!

It's hard to tell what just then was the matter,
　For the baby was the only one innocent there:
And Annie flushed up like a full-blown peony,
　And Samuel turned red to the roots of his hair.
So the question is this—you can answer it, maybe—
Did Annie kiss Sam, or did *both* kiss the baby?

A ROGUE.

GRANDMA was nodding, I rather think;
　Harry was sly and quick as a wink;
He climbed in the back of her great arm-chair
And nestled himself very snugly there.
Grandma's dark locks were mingled with white,
And quickly this fact came to his sight;
A sharp twinge soon she felt at her hair,
And woke with a start to find Harry there.
"Why, what are you doing, my child?" she said;
He answered, "I'se pulling a basting-fread!"

THE EGGS THAT NEVER HATCH.

THERE'S a young man on the corner,
　Filled with life and strength and hope,
Looking far beyond the present,
　With the whole world in his scope.
He is grasping at to-morrow,
　That phantom none can catch,
To-day is lost.　He's waiting
　For the eggs that never hatch.

There's an old man over yonder,
　With a worn and weary face,
With searching anxious features,
　And weak, uncertain pace.

He is living in the future,
 With no desire to catch
The golden Now. He's waiting
 For the eggs that never hatch.

There's a world of men and women,
 With their life's work yet undone,
Who are sitting, standing, moving
 Beneath the same great sun;
Ever eager for the future,
 But not content to snatch
The Present. They are waiting
 For the eggs that will never hatch.

THE RESCUE OF MR. FIGG.

MR. TIMOTHY FIGG got lost in the fog,
 While looking for cranberries out in the bog;
  And so he sat down
  And scratched on his crown,
In order to hasten the rise of a plan
By which he might get to the precincts of man;
  And then it befell,
  While held in his spell,
That all that he uttered was "Well! well!"

While thus in grave study, with eyes on the ground,
He heard, to his great satisfaction, a sound;
  And on through the fog
  Ran a little brown dog,
And after him ran Mr. Timothy Figg,
With such haste that his foot caught a vine or a twig,
  And pulled off a shoe
  In deep mud like glue;
And all that he muttered was "Whew! whew!"

The little dog led to a little neat cot,
And Mr. Figg knocked, though the house he knew not,
      For the fog hung low down.
      To the door came Miss Brown,
Mr. Figg's old-time love—once they loved till there came
A quarrel that parted their hearts like a flame.
      And wasn't it queer
      To find her right here?
And all that he uttered was "Dear! dear!"
Miss Brown then implored Mr. Figg to come in;

And the crest-fallen bachelor, damp to the skin,
      One shoe in the mud,
      With a pat and a thud
Walked in through the hall to the fire that blazed;
And sat there a-drying, with senses quite dazed;
      And then with sweet cheer
      Miss Brown drew up near;
And much that they uttered was "Dear! dear!"

THE COBBLER.

[This selection may be rendered very effective, if the reader, following the meaning of the text, should imitate the movements of a cobbler, bending forward, stitching and fitting, sewing motion, boring a hole, sticking in pegs, and hammering with fingers.]

WANDERING up and down one day,
    I peeped into a window over the way;
And putting his needle through and through,
There sat a cobbler making a shoe,

    For the world he cares never the whisk of a broom;
    All he wants is his elbow-room,
    Rap-a-tap-tap, tick-a-tack-too,
    This is the way he makes a shoe.

Over lasts of wood, his bits of leather
He stretches and fits, then sews together;
He puts his waxed-ends through and through,
And still as he stitches, his body goes too.

For the world he cares never the whisk of a broom;
All he wants is his elbow-room,
Rap-a-tap-tap, tick-a-tack-too,
This is the way he makes a shoe.

With his little sharp awl he makes a hole
Right through the upper and through the sole,
He puts in one peg, or he puts in two,
And chuckles and laughs as he hammers them through

For the world he cares never the whisk of a broom;
All he wants is his elbow-room,
Rap-a-tap-tap, tick-a-tack-too,
This is the way he makes a shoe.

IRISH COQUETRY.

SAYS Patrick to Biddy, "Good mornin', me dear,
  It's a bit av a sacret I've got for yer ear;
It's yersel' that is lukin' so charmin' the day,
That the heart in me breast is fast slippin' away."
"'Tis you that kin flatther," Miss Biddy replies,
And throws him a glance from her merry blue eyes.

"Arrah thin," cries Patrick, "'tis thinkin' av you
That's makin' me heartsick, me darlint, that's thrue!
  Sure I've waited a long while to tell ye this same,
And Biddy Maloney'll be sich a foine name."
Cries Biddy, "Have done wid yer talkin', I pray;
Shure me heart's not me own for this many a day!

"I gave it away to a good-lookin' boy,
Who thinks there is no one like Biddy Maloy;
So don't bother me, Pat; jist be aisy," says she.
"Indade, if ye'll let me, I will that!
It's a bit av a flirt that ye are on the sly;
I'll not trouble ye more, but I'll bid ye good-by."

"Arrah, Patrick," cries Biddy, "an' where are ye goin'?
Shure it isn't the best av good manners ye'er showin'
To leave me so suddint!" "Och, Biddy," says Pat,
"Ye have knocked the cock-feathers jist out av me hat!"
"Come back, Pat!" says she. "What fur, thin?" says he.
"Bekase I meant you all the time, sir!" says she.

A SUMMER DECEIT.

OH, he (so he said) was a millionaire,
 And she was a banker's daughter;
At least, she said she was, as they strolled
 On the sandy beach by the water.

They talked of the wealth that each one had,
 And their future seemed much brighter—
And then he returned to his job as a clerk,
 And she to her old typewriter.

AIN'T HE CUTE.

ARRAYED in snow-white pants and vest
 And other raiment fair to view,
 I stood before my sweetheart Sue—
The charming creature I love best.
 "Tell me, and does my costume suit?"
I asked that apple of my eye,
And then the charmer made reply—
 "Oh, yes, you do look awful cute!"

Although I frequently had heard
   My sweetheart vent her pleasure so,
I must confess I did not know,
   The meaning of that favorite word.

But presently at window side
   We stood and watched the passing throng,
   And soon a donkey passed along
With ears like sails extending wide.
And gazing at the doleful brute
   My sweetheart gave a merry cry—
   I quote her language with a sigh—
"O Charlie, ain't he awful cute?"

WHAT ADAM MISSED.

ADAM never knew what 'twas to be a boy,
   To wheedle pennies from a doting sire,
With which to barter for some pleasing toy,
   Or calm the rising of a strong desire,

To suck an orange.   Nor did he
   E'er cast the shuttlecock to battledoor;
Nor were his trousers ever out at knee,
   From playing marbles on the kitchen floor.

He never skated o'er the frozen rill,
   When winter's covering o'er the earth was spread;
Nor ever glided down the slippery hill,
   With pretty girls upon his trusty sled.

He never swung upon his father's gate,
   Or slept in sunshine on the cellar door,
Nor roasted chestnuts at the kitchen grate,
   Nor spun his humming top upon the floor.

He ne'er amused himself with rows of bricks,
    So set, if one fall, all come down;
Nor gazed delighted at the funny tricks
    Of harlequin or traveling circus clown.

By gradual growth he never reached the age
    When cruel Cupid first invokes his art,
And stamps love's glowing lesson, page by page,
    Upon the tablets of a youngling's heart.

He never wandered forth on moonlight nights,
    With her he loved above all earthly things:
Nor tried to mount old Pindar's rocky heights,
    Because he fancied love had lent him wings.

He never tripped it o'er the ball-room floor,
    Where love and music intertwine their charms,
Nor wandered listless by the sandy shore,
    Debarred the pleasures of his lady's arms.

For Adam,—so at least it has been said
    By many an ancient and a modern sage—
Before a moment of his life had fled,
    Was fully *thirty years of age!*

THE RETORT.

OLD Birch, who taught the village school,
    Wedded a maid of homespun habit;
He was stubborn as a mule,
    And she was playful as a rabbit.
Poor Kate had scarce become a wife
    Before her husband sought to make her
The pink of country polished life,
    And prim and formal as a Quaker.

One day the tutor went abroad,
  And simple Katie sadly missed him:
When he returned, behind her lord
  She slyly stole and fondly kissed him.
The husband's anger rose, and red
  And white his face alternate grew.
"Less freedom, ma'am!" Kate sighed and said,
  "O, dear! I didn't know 'twas you."

PAT'S WISDOM.

TIM DOLAN and his wife, wan night,
  Were drinkin' av the crayture,
Whin something started up a fight,
And they wint at it right an' tight,
  According to their nature.

O'Grady and mesilf stood near,
  Expecting bloody murther.
Says he to me: "Let's interfere."
But I pretending not to hear,
  Moved off a little further.

"Lave off, ye brute," says he to Tim;
  "No man wud sthrike a lady."
But both the Dolans turned on him,
And in a whist the two av them
  Were wallopin' O'Grady.

That night whin I was home, in bed,
  Remimbering this token,
I took the notion in my head
That the wisest word I iver said
  Was the one that wasn't spoken.

BE IN EARNEST.

NEVER be ashamed to say, "I do not know." Men will then believe you when you say, "I do know." Never be ashamed to say, "I can't afford it;" "I can't afford to waste time in the idleness to which you invite me;" or "I can't afford the money you ask me to spend." Never affect to be other than you are—either wiser or richer.

Learn to say "No" with decision; "Yes" with caution. "No" with decision whenever it resists temptation; "Yes" with caution whenever it implies a promise; for a promise once given is a bond inviolable.

A man is already of consequence in the world when it is known that we can implicitly rely upon him. Often have I known a man to be preferred in stations of honor and profit because he had this reputation; when he said he knew a thing, he knew it; and when he said he would do a thing, he did it. BULWER LYTTON.

THE MEN.

MRS. DUNIWAY of the New Northwest, at a literary reunion at Salem, Oregon, "toasted" the men as follows: "God bless 'em! They halve our joys, they double our sorrows, they treble our expenses, they quadruple our cares, they excite our magnamity, they increase our self-respect, they awake our enthusiasm, they arouse our affections, they control our property and out-manœuvre us in everything. This would be a very dreary world without 'em. In fact, I may say, without prospect of successful contradiction, that without 'em it would not be much of a world anyhow. We love 'em, and the dear beings can't help it; we control 'em and the precious fellows don't know it.

"As husbands they're always convenient, though not always on hand; as beaux they are by no means 'matchless.' They are most agreeable visitors; they are handy at state fairs and indispensable at oyster saloons. They are splendid as escorts for some other fellow's wife or sister, and as friends they are better than women. As our fathers, they are inexpressibly grand. A man may be a failure in business, a wreck in constitution, not enough to boast of as a beauty, nothing as a legislator for woman's rights, and even not very brilliant as a member of the press; but if he is our own father we overlook his shortcomings and cover his peccadilloes with the divine mantle of charity."

A CONTRAST.

AT her easel, brush in hand,
  Clad in silk attire,
Painting "sunsets" vague and grand
  (Clumsy clouds of fire!)
Flaxen hair in shining sheaves;
  Pink and pearly skin;
Fingers, which, like lily leaves,
  Neither toil nor spin;—
At her belt a sun-flower bound,
  Daisies on the table,
Plaques and panels all around—
  That's æsthetic Mabel!

In the kitchen, fork in hand,
  Clad in coarse attire,
Dishing oysters, fried and panned,
  From a blazing fire:
Dusty hair in frowsy knots;—
  Worn and withered skin;—
Fingers brown and hard as nuts,
  (When the frosts begin;)—
Baking-board, one side aground;
  Washtub, on the other;
Pots and skillets all around,—
  That is Mabel's mother!

ELEANOR C. DONNELLY.

A TIRESOME CALLER.

YOUNG SPOONOGLE never knows when to leave when he calls on a young lady; he likes the sound of his own voice so well that he talks on and on, while the poor girl grows light-headed with the tax on her strength and wishes the mantle-piece of Elijah would fall on the tiresome caller.

There is a young lady in a certain city who made up her mind to give Spoonogle a lesson. So one Sunday night when he called, she was as cordial as possible up to eleven o'clock. Then, having had a four-volume history of Spoonogle's life, with an extended account of his influence in politics and business, she began to get dizzy and have a ringing in her ears. At that moment her young brother rushed into the room, and said hurriedly :

"Pa wants the morning papers, sis!"

"Look in the vestibule, Willie," she answered gently. "I think I heard the boy leaving them some hours ago."

Spoonogle never took the hint, but drawled on about one thing and another in which the oft repeated letter I, as usual, bore a conspicuous part.

The next interruption was the head of the house, who entered briskly rubbing his hands. "Good morning—good morning," he said cheerily. "Ha! Spoonogle, you're out early. Well, 'early bird catches the worm.' It's going to be a fine day, from present appearances."

Spoonogle was dazed, but he concluded the old man had been drinking, and sat back with a "Come one, come all, this rock shall fly from its firm base as soon as yours truly" air that was decided and convincing.

A half hour passed away, and the good mother hurried in.

"Dear me! I'm late," she said as she entered, "I smelled the coffee an hour ago and knew breakfast was waiting; but—oh! Good morning, Mr. Spoonogle!" Then the sweet youth took the hint, and drawing himself together, he got out into the hall and opened the front door, just as the hired girl rung a bell, and the small boy yelled "Breakfast!" over the banisters.

Dialogues and Tableaux.

S HORT plays afford an excellent entertainment for special occasions in
schools, lodges and private parlors. As an educational agent the amateur
drama cannot be too highly esteemed; for it teaches the young performer
elocution, gesticulation, ease of manner, and a certain knowledge of human
emotions and passions which could hardly be acquired elsewhere. A few plain
directions for presenting short plays will be of service.

THE STAGE.—The first thing to be looked to is the stage, which may be constructed at a trifling expense, so as to be taken up and laid down in a few minutes,
and at any time. All that is necessary is a number of stout boards, such as flooring
is ordinarily made of, three or four beams of sufficient strength to support the actors,
furniture, etc., and twice as many boxes as beams. These boxes should be made
for the purpose, of thick plank, and should be from one to two feet in height,
according to the size of the room—the larger the room, the higher the stage, of
course. Place the boxes firmly, so as to support the ends of the beams; lay the
floor-boards evenly upon them, and when these are covered with a carpet the stage
is complete. To conceal the opening underneath, and to hide the front boxes, a
strip of some dark muslin may be tacked upon the edge of the boards and allowed
to fall to the floor.

THE CURTAIN.—The next thing of importance is the curtain, behind whose
friendly expanse the young comedians may arrange their scenes, and which may
close silently upon their histrionic triumphs. This should be made of some soft
stuff—the heavier the better—and should, if possible, be of the classic color, green,
so long considered sacred to stage-curtains. Yet any dark color will serve the
purpose.

Although much has been said in favor of draw-curtains, for school purposes and
private theatricals generally, the drop-curtain is much the best, and the easiest to
arrange. A light wooden frame should be made, tolerably firm at the joints, and
just as wide as the stage, to the front part of which it should be attached. This
frame is merely three sides of a square, and the curtain is to be strongly nailed to
the top piece. A stiff wire should be run along the lower edge of the curtain, and
a number of rings attached to the back of it, in squares—say three rows, of four
rings each, extending from top to bottom. Three cords are now fastened to the
wire, and, passing through the rings, are run over three pulleys on the upper piece
of the frame.

7—S C.

The ends of the cords may be gathered together, and held by the person who officiates as prompter. On pulling them, if the pulleys and rings are properly adjusted, the curtain will be found to rise easily, in lateral folds

COSTUMES.—Almost any household contains a sufficient variety of furniture and "properties" for any indoor scene, and a little ingenuity will produce a fair theatrical wardrobe from very common material. These things, of course, depend upon the piece to be performed, the taste of the actors, and other circumstances. The costume, for example, of a brigand, may be gotten up without difficulty, although it is one of the most picturesque. A common black felt hat, with the left side fastened up by a showy buckle, holding a black ostrich plume—a short velvet or woollen jacket with brass buttons (easily sewed on for the occasion)—a gay scarf bound several times around the waist, with a large knot and long ends, and a brace of pistols thrust in it—a pair of knee breeches (made by cutting off the legs of an old pair of pantaloons), with a knot of red ribbon at the knees, and long stockings—a pair of pumps, with metal buckles, and a quantity of paste jewelry, chains, etc., make a very respectable brigand's costume, at the expense of next to nothing. This is merely one instance among many that might be mentioned, and will illustrate the ease with which the "tinselled fascination of the stage" may be mimicked by the home fireside.

THE MAKING UP.—A still more important part of dramatic preparation is what is technically termed the "making up" of the characters, and one which requires some practice and observation. This is the painting and shading of faces, the adaptation of wigs, etc., to make the young look old, the plump lean, etc.

For the "making up" of any variety of different faces, a box of good water colors, a little fine chalk, some camel's-hair pencils, and dry rouge are wanted. If a comical expression is required, mix a reddish-brown tint with the water-colors, stand before a mirror, assume the desired "broad grin," and trace the wrinkles produced, with a fine brush of the brown tint. This will fix the line which your face requires, to give it the expression, much more naturally than you could do it by following any of the rules current among artists. The same may be done with frowns, smirks, simpers, scowls, and all other marked contortions of feature.

Rouge should be applied with the forefinger—a much better implement than the traditional hare's-foot—and should be softly graded off upon the cheek. Chalk should be very sparingly used. Burnt cork is very effective for black eyes, or for representing leanness, by applying a very faint tint underneath the eyes, on the sides of the cheeks, and under the lower lip. A strong mark running from the corner of the nose down towards the corner of the mouth, on each side, is a good sign of age or emaciation, but these points are best learned by observing different faces. Moustaches and beards, when slight, should be made with India-ink and a fine pencil. A few sets of false ones, of real hair, however, as also a few wigs of various colors and patterns, will be found a great addition to the wardrobe.

CAREFUL PREPARATION.—One of the most imperative of all rules which we can lay down—and one which applies to professional as well as amateur per-formers—is, "learn your parts *thoroughly*." Without this, no drama or lighter play can be well acted, or be interesting to the audience. Each performer should write out his own part, with the "cues" or words which come directly before his own speeches, and should commit *every word literally*. When the performer hears the words of the cue, knowing them by heart, they instantly suggest the speech to follow.

IN AND OUT.—The exits and entrances will be found somewhat difficult of management, in some rooms, and windows, or even closets, will occasionally have to be used—the latter, especially, for very short absences from the stage. A simple way of making one door serve for two exits is by placing a screen in front of it, at the back of the stage, and retiring behind, or issuing from, the ends of it. This screen will be found very useful in many pieces, and we would suggest that where such entertainments are popular it is worth while to have one constructed. It is simply made of wooden frames, some six feet high by three wide, hinged together and covered with cloth or wall-paper.

FOOTLIGHTS.—To secure a better illumination, a row of small lamps is often placed along the front of the stage, with a tin reflector between each and the audience. These reflectors may consist simply of a curved piece of tin, with a socket at the bottom for holding the candle.

EFFECTS.—Many striking effects may easily be produced that will add much to the seccess of a performance. Thunder is imitated by vigorously shaking a large piece of thin sheet iron to produce the rattle ; a bass-drum can be made to closely resemble the mutterings of a storm, and both together will produce the crash. *Lightning* is imitated by blowing a handful of powdered rosin through the flame of a lamp. The *sound of rain* is imitated by a revolving drum filled with peas or shot, which strike among a number of small pegs driven for the pur-pose, or by alternately raising and lowering the end of a long box containing peas, the bottom stuck full of pegs. *Snow* is represented by small pieces of paper dropped from above. *Mist* is imitated by allowing a curtain of thin white gauze or mosquito-netting to hang in front of the performers. *Vanishing a scene* is effected by dropping thin curtains of gauze one after another. *Colored fires* are often employed in tableaux, etc. Burning a little alcohol upon thoroughly dried nitrate of strontia in an iron vessel gives a crimson light ; upon nitrate of barytes, a yellow flame ; boracic acid or nitrate of copper, a green light ; on muriate of copper, an orange color. In these great care should be taken. A *wizard flame* for supernatural effects is produced by burning a solution of alcohol or oil and common salt, but all other lights in the room should be turned down. This gives a sallow, deathly hue to every face and dulls nearly every color. *High lights* are produced by placing at the side of the stage a lamp in a box lined with tin, the light directed upon any desired part of the stage or scenery.

Rehearsals.—After the parts are well committed, rehearsals should be held to fix the whole firmly in the mind and to secure ease in postures and acting. If possible, obtain the services of a competent critic to drill in modulation and naturalness of manner. Position upon the stage throughout should be attended to, that the players may not interfere with one another, and that the grouping be artistic and pleasing. Every detail of the acting should be carefully practiced.

Prompter.—At every performance some one with a book should act as prompter and stage manager. He should see that the scenes are properly arranged, the properties in order, and, with a bell, should ring up the curtain and signal for it to fall.

The Characters.—Every performer should assume the exact character he is to present. Above everything else, naturalness is required. Make the part your own. Take it with ease, yet with spirit and life-likeness. Do not be stiff or stilted. Lack of animation will spoil the performance. Every performer should be alert and attend strictly to business. The entire presentation should be alive with action. Speak with sufficient volume to enable all in the room to hear. Give the "asides" in a lower tone, yet distinctly. Make the pauses between the acts as brief as possible.

Tableaux.—Sometimes it is thought advisable to fill up a portion of the evening, or the time between acts, with tableaux, pantomime, etc. Tableaux require some time in arranging, but are very effective. Allegorical and other subjects may be chosen, the figures properly posed so as to make a tasty picture, and the curtain drawn for an instant only. *Statuary* tableaux representing single figures or groups, neatly draped in white and brightly illuminated, are very pretty. In all tableaux, of course, the figures must remain perfectly immovable when in view of the audience.

Pantomimes.—In these the story is acted out by signs and gestures, not a word being spoken. Ingenious players can make it a realistic, and, if desired, very laughable performance. Take some familiar subject, such as "Washington and His Hatchet," "Bluebeard," "William Tell," etc. Or take some well-known play and enact the most striking scenes.

Shadow Pantomimes.—Suspend a white curtain between players and audience, and place a strong light upon the floor back of the performers, thus throwing their shadows upon the screen. Turn down all other lights in the room. Much amusement may be created by allowing the actors to enter and retire by leaping over the lamps, the appearance upon the curtain then being that of players dropping from above and rising through the ceiling.

Following these plain instructions, and selecting a bright, entertaining dialogue, there is every reason to expect the performance will be a complete success.

THE HAUNTED CHAMBER.

[For this little performance an empty picture frame will be required. The scenery otherwise can be easily changed by a mere alteration of furniture.]

CHARACTERS:

GEORGE McDONNEL . . . . *A Great Catch.*

JAMES BROWN . . . . *A Volunteer (not too wise).*

JOHNNY GRANT . . . . *An Etonian.*

MRS. GRANT . . . .

ETHEL . . . . *Her Daughter, Cousin to* GEORGE McDONNEL.

ALICE . . . . *A Young Lady Visitor.*

MARY . . . . *A Poor Relation who has to earn her own living.*

SCENE I.

Drawing-room, with fire-place, etc., etc. Winter. ALICE *and* ETHEL *discovered seated by the fire, dressed extravagantly, in the height of the fashion. They each hold a novel, and appear absorbed by it. At the table* MARY *is seated, working or knitting.*

ETHEL. Oh, Alice! She has actually pushed him over the chalk pit and killed him; and —— imagine! he fell on the head of a gypsy sitting beneath, who was crushed by the descending body!

ALICE. Horrid! The poor gypsy! What *did* she do afterward?

ETHEL. Oh, she went home to dinner, after gathering a bunch of bee-orchis flowers for a bouquet.

ALICE. How intensely interesting!

ETHEL. What is your book about? Is it as enthralling as mine?

ALICE. Well, no; I don't fancy so. You see, not understanding bankers' business, and railways, and directors, and all that, I can't feel so amused in reading about the swindling, but I fancy it will get better by and by. I think Delaval will be obliged to poison the whole Board of Directors in self-defense—he has forged to such an extent [*yawns*]. How Mary sits plodding at that knitting.

ETHEL. Oh, you see mamma does not approve of novels for Mary;

she says Mary must read heavy books. She's going to be a governess, you know.

ALICE (*kindly*). Poor girl!—but she might read a novel at her leisure, as well as knit. Here, Mary, I will lend you mine. [*Offers the book.*]

MARY (*smiling*). No, thank you, dear Alice. I don't care to read about such wretched people. It would make me quite unhappy.

ALICE. Ah, that's because you don't read enough novels. The first sensation novel *I* read made me feel quite unhappy; but now the most horrid things make no impression on me. I can't get them dreadful enough.

MARY. Dear Alice, are you not afraid of growing quite unfeeling? One's sensibility must be completely deadened by those books, if that is the case.

ETHEL (*mockingly*). *Sensibility!* Well, Mary, you *are* amusing! Who dreams of sensibility nowadays? Wouldn't Johnny chaff you, if he were here?

JOHNNY (*who has entered unperceived*). No, he wouldn't, Thel. It is quite a blessing to find a girl who can feel at all, nowadays.

ETHEL. What would you have? We have done with feminine weakness. The women of this country, Johnny, "nowadays," as you elegantly say, are equal to leading a forlorn hope.

JOHNNY (*sarcastically*). Yes, I am quite aware of that fact. Mothers and daughters do so every season. By-the-bye, where is my mother?

ETHEL. She has driven to the railway station, to meet and bring back Cousin George and his friend. I expect them now every minute.

JOHNNY. What a muff that Brown is! I wonder he became a volunteer. I should think he would be afraid of the sound of his own rifle. I can't make out why George is so civil to him.

MARY. I heard a lady say one day that Mr. Brown is an excellent son, and that his nervous, bashful manner hides excellent qualities.

ETHEL. Johnny, tell me directly what sort of fellow Cousin George has grown. I haven't seen him since he was a schoolboy.

JOHNNY (*aside to* MARY). He's a great catch, you know! My mother means Ethel to have him. [*Aloud.*] Oh, a fast man, rather. *You* will just suit him, Ethel. He likes a girl who could lead a forlorn hope [*laughing*].

ETHEL. I am very glad of that—I hate milk-sops. I like a terrible, resolved, fearless man. A kind of Napoleon the First.

JOHNNY (*laughing*). That's George, exactly. But, hark! there's a ring at the bell. Here they come.

Enter Mrs. GRANT, GEORGE *and* JAMES.

MRS. GRANT. Ethel—your Cousin George. Alice—my nephew, Mr. McDonnel. [*They exchange the civilities of greeting, etc.*] Do you find Ethel much changed, George?

GEORGE. Yes, indeed. She was not above so high when we met last time; she played with a doll then, I fancy.

ETHEL (*eagerly*). Oh, no, George; I never played with a doll, except to make a hammer of one. I was never so foolish!

GEORGE (*smiling*). Were you not? Well, I confess to a top and hoop myself.

MRS. GRANT. It is so near dinner that I think you must leave the discussion of your childish days till by and by. Ethel, dear, I must ask you to take my place at the table; I am suffering from so severe a headache that I must go and lie down. Mr. Brown and George will excuse me.

ETHEL (*indifferently*). Very well, mamma; we will take care of ourselves.

MARY. Let me come with you, dear aunt, and make a cup of tea for you.

GEORGE. I am very sorry for you, aunty mine. I hope your pain has not been caused by the cold air.

MRS. GRANT. Oh, no; I often suffer in the same way. Come, Mary. I have a good little nurse in my niece.

ETHEL (*shrugging her shoulders*). I am sure that is lucky for me, for I am utterly helpless in a sick room. You can't think what a baby I am, and how useless I feel in one [*to* GEORGE].

GEORGE. I can believe the fact. You would doubtless be sadly out of place as a nurse.

ETHEL. Oh, *my* place is the saddle! Alice, come with me: it is time to dress, and I have something to tell you. Stop, mamma, please stop. [*Speaks to her aside.*] Don't keep Mary! Send her to do my hair. No one can make it look as well as she does.

MRS. GRANT. Very well, my dear. [*Exeunt.*

SCENE II.

THE DRAWING ROOM AGAIN.

Enter, after dinner, GEORGE, ETHEL, JAMES, ALICE *and* MARY.

GEORGE. I am very sorry poor Aunt Eleanor has a headache, Ethel.

ETHEL. It is the change of weather, I fancy, that has caused it. What a convenient scapegoat the east wind is!

*The young people are to stand together about the room—*JAMES *conversing in by-play with* ALICE; MARY *with* JOHNNY—ETHEL *and* GEORGE *advance to the front.*

GEORGE. Do you ride much, Cousin Ethel?

ETHEL. *Rather*, I should think! I hunt pretty regularly. I can't think what life would be without hunting.

GEORGE. I hope to go out with you on Thursday. I think that is the day Johnny mentioned.

ETHEL. Yes; you'll find this a rather stiff country for it; ditches deep and wide, but that only adds to the fun.

GEORGE. I see you are a spirited girl, as you promised to be when you made a hammer of your doll.

ETHEL. You flatter me. But oh, Cousin George, what *would* the young ladies of to-day have done had they been born in the days when girls had to make puddings, and sew!

GEORGE. Really, I can't imagine.

ETHEL. Things are so different with us! Women have spirit and courage—Cousin George, do you remember our haunted room?

GEORGE. Yes, quite well. I have played hide-and-seek in it many times, in spite of the ghost. Has the apparition been making itself unpleasant lately?

ETHEL. Well, yes—that is, to say, we really *want* the room, and yet mamma does not like it to be used. Johnny and I incline to think that she *believes* in the ancestral ghost, she is so averse to the chamber being occupied.

GEORGE. How like you are to the portrait of your paternal ancestress hanging in that chamber, Ethel!

ETHEL. Oh, yes! So every one says who has seen it. Now, George, it is very aristocratic to have a ghost in the family, I know; it shows one had ancestors, and all that sort of thing. But I *do* want the room for a charade; and it came into my head just before dinner that if *you* (who are so brave) would pass the night in it, the ghost-story would no longer be believed, and we might have the room. I said so to Alice.

GEORGE. My dear coz, I should have no objection to sleep there; but the room has no bed in it, has it? It used to be quite unfurnished.

ETHEL. So it is now; but we could arrange a sofa and a little furniture; and as mamma is in bed she would know nothing about the matter and could not object, and you would have laid the ghost by to-morrow.

GEORGE (*laughing*). Well, I have no objections to try, if you wish it, but ——

ETHEL (*eagerly*). Alice! Mary! Hear him. My cousin has consented to sleep in the haunted chamber! [*She claps her hands.*] I feel like a lady of the olden time sending her knight on a perilous adventure.

JOHNNY. What stuff! George, take my advice and don't do it. You'll be wretchedly uncomfortable, and may ——

ETHEL. Be quiet, sir! A man of spirit disdains comfort.

BROWN (*timidly.*) But if it should be damp, Miss Grant—uninhabited rooms ——

ETHEL (*with great scorn*). Oh, *you* are not asked to do it, Mr.

Brown, and *I* don't believe in rheumatism. It's settled. **You will** do it, won't you, George, for *my* sake? [*Coquettishly.*]

GEORGE. For *your* sake, my dear cousin, I would do much more.

ETHEL. Charming! Then I shall run away and order them to make preparations for you there. Alice, dearest, come and help. [*They leave the room.*]

BROWN (*aside to* JOHNNY *but heard by* MARY). My dear Johnny, George is very delicate, and a very sensitive, imaginative fellow; do persuade him not to sit up all night in a damp room after a long journey.

JOHNNY (*shrugging his shoulders*). It is no concern of mine. He is old enough to take care of himself. [*Aloud.*] I say, Brown, come and see my retriever; he beats yours out and out. Mary, make yourself agreeable to George while we are gone.   [*Exit.*

GEORGE. Cousin Mary, you are so grown that I did not recognize you when first I arrived. Ethel told me after dinner all about your great sorrow. My dear little cousin, I am so sorry for you.

MARY. Thank you, Mr. McDonnel.

GEORGE. Why are you so formal? Why don't you call me George?

MARY. My aunt would not like it. She says I am only connected with you by marriage—not related.

GEORGE. Nay ——

MARY (*hurriedly*). Please never mind about it now. I have something I wish so much to say to you, and I am afraid Ethel will come back.

GEORGE (*approaches the table*). A secret! What can it be?

MARY. Only this: you are to be played a practical joke to-night in the haunted room, and I have heard my dear father say that even the bravest people may suffer from such folly.

GEORGE. You are very thoughtful and kind, my dear Mary. What is the trick to be? A ghost with a turnip face?

MARY. Oh, no! I should not have been afraid for you with that · it is a much more cunning and terrible affair. Cousin Ethel and Alice read those horrid sensation stories till they think of —— Oh! here they are! Hush. [*Lays her fingers on her lips.*]

Enter ALICE, JOHNNY *and* ETHEL, *laughing.* JAMES *follows them at a little distance.*

ETHEL. George! The housekeeper has promised to make your room comfortable.

JOHNNY. It is all arranged delightfully, and I hope to hear to-morrow at breakfast that George has quieted the ghost, and that we may have the room for our Christmas charade.

GEORGE. I shall do all in my power. I am to be allowed pistols, I suppose?

ETHEL. Dear me! I fear there are none in the house, unless Johnny has a pair.

JOHNNY. No. I have lent mine to Tom D'Urfey.

ALICE. But perhaps Mr. Brown has brought his rifle?

MARY. Pray do not use firearms, Mr. McDonnel; my aunt would be frightened into fits if she heard them at night.

GEORGE. Don't be afraid; I will employ more effective weapons. I have a certain charm for laying ghosts.

MARY. But I hope you are not at all nervous. I have heard such dreadful stories of people being frightened into idiocy.

GEORGE. I have no fear of that. Come, Cousin Ethel, let us all go and look at this haunted chamber, so that I may judge a little of the trial to which I shall be exposed. Then we will return, and I shall ask you for a song in reward for my self-devotion. [*Exeunt.*

SCENE III.

THE HAUNTED CHAMBER.

A housemaid arranging furniture. A toilet table with candles on it; a sofa, so placed that the person lying on it faces the portrait, which must be opposite the audience.

Enter ETHEL *and her party.*

GEORGE. I must allow that my chamber looks very comfortable, and has not at all a ghostly aspect. Now, Ethel, tell me about this fair ancestress of ours, so that if she should appear I may ask her pertinent questions. I never heard the legend, though I always knew that the room was said to be haunted.

ETHEL(*solemnly*). That portrait was painted by a young Italian artist with whom our great-great-great-great-aunt fell in love ; but he preferred her younger sister to herself. However, on the day appointed for his wedding with the latter he never appeared and was never heard of afterward. He had slept the previous night in this room ; but in the morning the window was open, and the bridegroom gone.

GEORGE. Did he carry off any of the plate?

ETHEL. Nonsense! Our aunt, in despair, had her picture, which he had painted (the last souvenir of the lost one) hung in this room. She died. The chamber has been haunted ever since.

ALICE. I dare say she poisoned him.

JOHNNY. But, then, what could she have done with the body?

ALICE. Oh! there are many ways of disposing of that ——

GEORGE. You make me shudder! Any one would think you quite experienced in such performances. But, Ethel, in what manner does the ghost appear?

ETHEL. *That* you will have to tell us.

GEORGE. The picture looks to me as if it were a little loose in the frame. [*He approaches it.*]

ETHEL (*drawing him back*). *Please*, don't touch it. Mamma would be vexed if we hurt it. And now, George, that you have seen your room, we will go back to the drawing-room and have some music, if you please. [*Exeunt.*

[*An interval, with music.*]

SCENE IV.

THE HAUNTED ROOM.

GEORGE (*seated at a table near the fire. He takes a letter from his pocket*). Let me see what little Mary has to tell me. She slipped this note into my hand when I said good-night to her. [*Opens it and reads*], " *E. has persuaded Johnny to take the portrait from its frame; it is loose in it now. At midnight she will seat herself in the frame and play Ghost. She arranged the trick while I was in her room before dinner. I was afraid you might be alarmed, or that, perhaps (guessing it was a trick), you would throw something at Ethel and hurt her.*" Good little thing! What a trick; and alas; what a fast girl is my cousin. Now I confess my little guardian here (*touching the note*) has taken my fancy. She possesses common sense and kindness; and she looked charmingly homelike and womanly sitting by the fireside working in her modest dress. She has read, too, and can appreciate well-written books. Ethel would tire one to death in a week with slang, horses and tennis. [*He stirs the fire.*] A table with wine and books!—quite in the orthodox Udolpho style. [*Takes up the book aud turns over a few leaves.*] Pshaw! a dressed-up Newgate Calendar! How can my aunt permit her daughter to read it?

*After reading awhile he lies down on the sofa and appears to sleep: a curtain falls for a moment or two over the portrait, then it is gently drawn up again.—Clock strikes twelve slowly.—*GEORGE *rises on his elbow and looks at the picture.—The eyes move—the head is raised—the finger beckons.*

GEORGE. A *Tableau Vivant,* by all that's lovely! Sleeping beauty in a new edition! My dear madame (*bowing profoundly*), I am glad to be present at your awakening. Your story is of a most affecting character. How that Italian fellow could be blind to so much beauty I can't conceive. Allow me to assure you that I am not. [*The picture becomes again immovable, except the eyes.*] We have long been wishing for some sleeping princess to awake, who would bring us back the womanly modesty and tender softness of the good old day once more. You, lady, who were (if you are not slandered) more fit to be heroine of one of your grand-niece's favorite books, have doubt-less repented of your crimes, if you committed any, bitterly by the time; therefore, at the risk of your crumbling to dust in my arms, I mean to bestow on you a grand-nephew's pardon and a tender embrace.

He rushes forward.   A scream is uttered, and the picture-frame falls on its face into the room.

GEORGE.   So!—just as I anticipated—the ghost is laid!

[*Curtain falls.*

SCENE V.

MORNING—HAUNTED CHAMBER.

Re-enter the performers ; GEORGE *by the side of his* AUNT.

GEORGE.   I am sorry that the noise last night should have alarmed you, my dear aunt ; but you see the cause of it.   The ghost is laid. The lady has descended from her frame, to return no more.   The promise of a kiss sufficed her.

MRS. GRANT.   What do you mean, George ?   What has become of the portrait ?   It is of great value.   Tell me directly what all this absurdity means.

GEORGE.   It means, dear aunt, that you have let my pretty Cousin Ethel read nonsense and act boyishly too long.   But for a friendly warning I might have been seriously alarmed last night ; braver men than I profess to have suffered severely from the sort of ordeal to which I would have been exposed.   Or, which is quite as likely, I might have thrown the nearest missile at hand at the head of the charming portrait.   Dear Ethel! pray don't play practical jokes again, even with Johnny's approval.

ETHEL.   Who *could* have told you ?   And, George, if you knew who it was, you were very rude indeed, and I shan't easily forgive you!

MRS. GRANT.   I really must beg to be told what has occurred.   I fear, dear Ethel, you have been very foolish.   [GEORGE *takes his aunt toward the picture, and appears to be telling her of the trick*.]

JOHNNY.   Well, the ghost is laid, and (*aside to* ETHEL) you have not the ghost of a chance of catching George. I can tell you!   It serves you right, too, I think.

ETHEL.   You mischievous little monster.

JOHNNY.   It's very fine to call me a monster, but a mischievous boy *isn't* one—he's only natural—a fast, bold girl is. I hope you will take warning. From something I heard George say when I was removing the picture for you, I am certain he will ask mother for Mary before Christmas is over. So that will be the catastrophe of your *Tableau Vivant.*

COURTSHIP UNDER DIFFICULTIES.

FOR TWO MALES AND ONE FEMALE.

[This may be made almost equally successful as a reading.]

Enter Snobbleton.

SNOBBLETON (*looking in the direction whence he has just come*). Yes, there is that fellow Jones, again. I declare, the man is ubiquitous. Wherever I go with my Cousin Prudence we stumble across him, or he follows her like her shadow. Do we take a boating? So does Jones. Do we wander on the beach? So does Jones. Go where we will, that fellow follows or moves before. Now, that was a cruel practical joke which Jones once played upon me at college. I have never forgiven him. But I would gladly make a pretense of doing so, if I could have my revenge. Let me see. Can't I manage it? He is head over ears in love with Prudence, but too bashful to speak. I half believe she is not indifferent to him, though altogether unacquainted. It may prove a match, if I cannot spoil it. Let me think. Ha! I have it! A brilliant idea! Jones, beware! But here he comes.

Enter Jones.

Jones (*not seeing* Snobbleton, *and delightedly contemplating a flower, which he holds in his hand*). Oh, rapture! what a prize! It was in her hair—I saw it fall from her queenly head. [*Kisses it every now and then*]. How warm are its tender leaves from having touched her neck! How doubly sweet is its perfume—fresh from the fragrance of her glorious locks! How beautiful! how—Bless me! here is Snobbleton. We are enemies!

Snobbleton (*advancing with an air of frankness*). Good morning, Jones—that is, if you will shake hands.

JONES.   What!—you forgive!   You really—

SNOBBLETON.   Yes, yes, old fellow!   All is forgotten.   You played me a rough trick; but let bygones be bygones.   Will you not bury the hatchet?

JONES.   With all my heart, my dear fellow!   [*They shake hands.*]

SNOBBLETON.   What is the matter with you, Jones?   You look quite grumpy—not by any means the same cheerful, dashing, rollicking fellow you were.

JONES.   Grumpy—what is that?   How *do* I look, Snobbleton?

SNOBBLETON.   Oh, not much out of the way.   Only a little shaky in the shanks, blue lips, red nose, cadaverous jaws, bloodshot eyes, yellow ——

JONES (*aghast*).   Bless me, you don't say so!   [*Aside.*]   Confound the man!   Here have I been endeavoring to appear romantic for the last month—and now to be called shaky-shanked, cadaverous—it is unbearable!

SNOBBLETON.   But never mind.   Cheer up, old fellow!   I see it all.   Egad!   I know what it is to be in ——

JONES.   Ah!   You can then sympathize with me.   You know what it is to be in ——

SNOBBLETON.   Of *course* I do!   Heaven preserve me from the toils!   What days of bitterness!

JONES.   What nights of bliss!

SNOBBLETON (*shuddering*).   And then the letters—the interminable letters.

JONES (*with rapture*).   Oh, yes, the letters!   The *billet doux!*

SNOBBLETON.   And the bills—the endless bills!

JONES (*in surprise*).   The bills?

SNOBBLETON.   Yes; and the bailiffs, the lawyers, the judge and the jury.

JONES.   Why, man, what are you talking about?   I thought you said you knew what it was to be in ——

SNOBBLETON.   In debt.   *To be sure* I did.

JONES.   Bless me!   I'm not in debt—never borrowed a dollar in my life.   Ah, me!   (*sighs*) it's worse than *that.*

A STUDY IN ATTITUDES

SHE HAD SO MANY CHILDREN SHE DIDN'T KNOW
WHAT TO DO

SNOBBLETON. Worse than that! Come, now, Jones, there is only one thing worse. You're surely not in love?

JONES. Yes, I am. [*With sudden feeling.*] Oh, Snobby, help me, help me! Let me confide in you.

SNOBBLETON (*with much emotion*). Confide in me! Certainly, my dear fellow! See! I do not shrink—I stand firm. [*Folds his arms in a determined posture.*] Blaze away!

JONES. Snobby, I—I love her.

SNOBBLETON. Whom?

JONES. Your cousin, Prudence.

SNOBBLETON. Ha! Prudence Angelina Winterbottom?

JONES. Now, don't be angry, Snobby! I don't mean any harm, you know. I—I—you know how it is.

SNOBBLETON. Harm! my dear fellow. Not a bit of it. Angry! Not at all. You have my consent, old fellow. Take her. She is yours. Heaven bless you both.

JONES. You are very kind, Snobby, but I haven't got *her* consent yet.

SNOBBLETON. Well, that *is* something to be sure. But, leave it all to me. She may be a little coy, you know; but, considering your generous overlooking of her unfortunate defect ——

JONES. Defect? You surprise me.

SNOBBLETON. What! and you did not know of it?

JONES. Not at all. I am astonished! Nothing serious, I hope.

SNOBBLETON. Oh, no, only a little. [*He taps his ear with his finger, knowingly.*] I see you understand it.

JONES. Merciful heaven! can it be? But, really is it serious?

SNOBBLETON. I should think it was.

JONES. What! But is she ever dangerous?

SNOBBLETON. Dangerous! Why should she be?

JONES (*considerably relieved*). Oh, I perceive! A mere airiness of brain—a gentle aberration—scorning the dull world—a mild—

SNOBBLETON. Zounds, man, she's not crazy!

JONES. My dear Snobby, you relieve me.

—S. C.

SNOBBLETON.   Slightly deaf.   That's all.

JONES.   Deaf!

SNOBBLETON.   As a lamppost.   That is, you must elevate your voice to a considerable pitch in speaking to her.

JONES.   Is it possible!   However, I think I can manage.   As, for instance, if it was my intention to make her a floral offering, and I should say (*elevating his voice considerably*), "Miss, will you make me happy by accepting these flowers?"   I suppose she could hear me, eh?   How would that do?

SNOBBLETON.   Pshaw!   Do you call that elevated?

JONES.   Well, how would this do?   [*Speak very loudly.*]   "Miss, will you make me happy ——"

SNOBBLETON.   Louder, shriller, man!

JONES.   "Miss, will you ——"

SNOBBLETON.   Louder, louder, or she will only see your lips move.

JONES (*almost screaming*).   "Miss, will you oblige me by accepting these flowers?"

SNOBBLETON.   There, that *may* do.   Still you want practice.   I perceive the lady herself is approaching.   Suppose you retire for a short time, and I will prepare her for the introduction.

JONES.   Very good.   Meantime, I will go down to the beach and endeavor to acquire the proper pitch.   Let me see: "Miss, will you oblige me ——"   [*Exit* JONES *still speaking.*

Enter PRUDENCE, *from other side.*

PRUDENCE.   Good morning, cousin.   Who was that, speaking so loudly?

SNOBBLETON.   Only Jones.   Poor fellow, he is so deaf that I suppose he fancies his own voice to be a mere whisper.

PRUDENCE.   Why, I was not aware of this.   Is he *very* deaf?

SNOBBLETON.   Deaf as a stone fence.   To be sure he does not use an ear-trumpet any more, but one must speak excessively high. Unfortunate, too, for I believe he is in love.

PRUDENCE (*with me emotion*).   In love! with whom?

SNOBBLETON.   Can't you guess?

PRUDENCE.   Oh no; I haven't the slightest idea.

SNOBBLETON.   With yourself!   He has been begging me to obtain him an introduction.

PRUDENCE.   Well, I have always thought him a nice-looking young man.   I suppose he would hear me if I was to say (*speaks loudly*), "Good morning, Mr. Jones?"

SNOBBLETON (*compassionately*).   *Do* you think he would hear *that?*

PRUDENCE.   Well, then, how would (*speaks very loudly*) "Good morning, Mr. Jones!"   How would that do?

SNOBBLETON.   Tush!   He would think you were speaking under your breath.

PRUDENCE (*almost screaming*).   "Good morning!"

SNOBBLETON.   A mere whisper, my dear cousin.   But here he comes.   Now, do try and make yourself audible.

Enter JONES.

SNOBBLETON (*speaking in a high voice*).   Mr. Jones, cousin.   Miss Winterbottom, Jones.   You will please excuse me for a short time. [*He retires, but remains in view.*]

JONES (*speaking shrill and loud, and offering some flowers*).   Miss, will you accept these flowers?   I plucked them from their slumber on the hill.

PRUDENCE (*in an equally high voice*).   Really, sir, I—I—

JONES (*aside*).   She hesitates.   It must be that she does not hear me.   [*Increasing his tones.*]   Miss, will you accept these flowers— FLOWERS?   I plucked them sleeping on the hill—HILL.

PRUDENCE (*also increasing her tone*).   Certainly, Mr. Jones.   They are beautiful—BEAU-U-TIFUL.

JONES (*aside*).   How she screams in my ear.   [*Aloud.*]   Yes, I plucked them from their slumber—SLUMBER, on the hill—HILL.

PRUDENCE (*aside*).   Poor man, what an effort it seems to him to speak.   [*Aloud.*]   I perceive you are poetical.   Are you fond of poetry. [*Aside.*] He hesitates. I must speak louder. [*In a scream.*] Poetry—POETRY—POETRY!

JONES (*aside*). Bless me, the woman would wake the dead! [*Aloud.*] Yes, Miss, I ad-o-r-e it.

SNOBBLETON (*solus from behind, rubbing his hands*). Glorious! glorious! I wonder how loud they *can* scream. Oh, vengeance, thou art sweet!

PRUDENCE. Can you repeat some poetry—POETRY.

JONES. I only know one poem. It is this:

> You'd scarce expect one of my age—AGE,
> To speak in public on the stage—STAGE.

PRUDENCE (*putting her lips to his ear and shouting.*) Bravo—bravo!

JONES (*in the same way*). Thank you! THANK ——

PRUDENCE (*putting her hands over her ears*) Mercy on us! Do you think I'm DEAF, sir?

JONES (*also stopping his ears*). And do you fancy *me* deaf, Miss?

[*They now speak in their natural tones.*]

PRUDENCE. Are you not, sir? You surprise me!

JONES. No, Miss. I was led to believe that *you* were deaf. Snobbleton told me so.

PRUDENCE. Snobbleton! Why he told me that *you* were deaf.

JONES. Confound the fellow! he has been making game of us Here he is. [*Perceiving Snobbleton.*] You shall answer for this, sir.

PRUDENCE. Yes, sir. You shall answer for this, sir.

SNOBBLETON (*advancing*). Ha! ha! ha! And to whom must I answer?

JONES (*they turn to the audience*). To these, our friends, whose ears are split.

SNOBBLETON. Well, then, the answer must be brief.

PRUDENCE (*to Jones*). But they, our friends, are making it.

JONES. I hear them, Miss. I am not deaf.

[*Curtain Falls.*]

HOW SHE CURED HIM.

FOR A GENTLEMAN AND TWO LADIES.

CHARACTERS:

UNCLE JOSEPH . . . . *An Invalid.*
THEODORA . . . . *His Niece.*
MRS. PERKINS . . . . *His Housekeeper.*

SCENE I.

To represent a kitchen. MRS. PERKINS *is washing dishes—*THEODORA *paring apples.*

MRS. PERKINS. It's a burning shame—so it is—the cross old curmudgeon! Nothing ails him but the hypo. He's jest as well as anybody if he only thought so. He keeps the house stirred up all the time;—and you, Miss Dora, are just killing yourself waiting on him.

DORA. Uncle is getting very nervous, it is true, but perhaps he is sicker than we think, Mrs. Perkins.

MRS. P. Land sakes! who wouldn't be nervous shet up in the house all the time? The old tyrant manages to keep us hopping and bounding. If he only took half as much exercise as he gives us he would be well enough, I'll warrant! There it goes again—that old cane thumping on the floor! What now, I wonder?

DORA. Yes, that's uncle calling—I must run up stairs and see what he wants.

MRS. P. (*to herself*). That girl makes a perfect little ninny of herself, humoring all his whims. I'd 'ike to see myself doing it for anybody.

SCENE II.

The sick room. UNCLE JOSEPH *in an easy chair with feet on a foot-rest. Enter* DORA.

UNCLE JOSEPH. Well, you have come at last, have you? I've been rapping on the floor till my arms are ready to fall out of their sockets. Are you all deaf downstairs, or has old Perkins forgotten that there is anybody here but herself and her snuff box?

Dora.   I'm very sorry, uncle.

Uncle J.   Actions speak louder than words.

Dora.   How do you feel now, Uncle Joseph?

Uncle J.   I'm worse.

Dora.   Are you?

Uncle J.   Flesh hot, pulse high, skin flushed—of course, I'm worse.   This confounded hot room is enough to throw anyone into a fever.   Open all the doors and windows—quick!   [*She obeys and then returns to receive his next orders.*]   Uh! do you want to freeze me to death—to blow me away?

Dora.   You told me to air the room, uncle.

Uncle J.   Shut the doors—put down the windows—draw the curtains, the sun hurts my eyes.

Dora.   Yes, uncle.   [*Goes out and returns.*]

Uncle J. (*hears a knocking*).   Who's that battering down that door?

Dora.   It's only a gentle knocking, uncle.

Uncle J.   Then I'm nervous.   Go and see who's there.

Dora (*returns*).   It is Major Crowfoot, uncle, he sends his compliments and wants to know how you are.

Uncle J.   Tell him to go to the deuce.

Dora.   Yes, uncle.   [*Goes out and returns soon.*]

Uncle J.   Well, what did he say?

Dora.   He seemed very much offended, uncle.

Uncle J.   Offended?   At what, pray?

Dora.   At being told to go to the deuce, I suppose.

Uncle J.   Girl, you didn't tell him that?

Dora.   Yes, I did.   You said yourself, "tell him to go to the deuce!"

Uncle J.   Dora, you're a fool.

Dora.   I'm very sorry, uncle.

Uncle J.   Get me some water gruel and be quick about it, too. A man must eat even if he is at death's door.   Oh dear!   Oh dear! what a senseless pack I've got around me!   [Dora *leaves.*]

wonder if that girl is getting crazy. Told Major Crowfoot that stuff. I'll bet he's hopping mad—don't blame him. Dora must be either a fool or a lunatic. Well, I can't help it now. Here I've got to lie day after day—never'll be any better as long as I must be agitated all the time by such pig-headed people as live under this roof.

DORA (*returns with the gruel*). Here's your gruel, uncle.

UNCLE J. (*tastes and throws down the spoon*). Trash! trash! insipid as dishwater! Throw it to the pigs.

DORA. Yes, uncle. [*Starts off with the gruel.*]

UNCLE J. Where are you going, Theodora?

DORA. To the pig pen, uncle.

UNCLE J. Girl, are you an idiot? The gruel is well enough, only Mrs. Perkins forgot the nutmeg.

DORA (*tasting*). But, uncle, it is as insipid as dishwater.

UNCLE J. Will you allow me to have an opinion of my own? It will be all right if that old crone, downstairs, will only add the nutmeg and give it another boil.

SCENE III.

DORA *enters the kitchen with the gruel.*

MRS. P. Well, what's wanted now, Miss Dora?

DORA. Uncle wishes you to boil the gruel a little more and add some nutmeg. His appetite is very poor, you know. He thinks he feels worse to-day.

MRS. P. He does, hey? Wal, hand it here, I'll see if I can fix it to his liking. The fussy old thing; nobody can please him. [*Stirs the gruel over the fire, then hands it to* DORA.] I wonder if it will do now?

DORA. I hope so. Oh dear! [*Leaves the room.*]

MRS. P. (*to herself*). I should think it was "Oh dear!" I'd like to know how many times she's run up and down stairs to-day! She will wait on him herself because she thinks, I s'pose, nobody else could stand it with him. Wal, I'm glad of it. I couldn't have the patience that dear child has, I'm sure.

Scene IV.

Dora *enters*.

Dora.   Here's your gruel, uncle.

Uncle J.   Why didn't you stay all day?   I never saw such a snail in all my life!

Dora.   Indeed, uncle, I hurried just as fast as I could.

Uncle J.   It's too late now.   I've lost all my appetite.

Dora.   Won't you have the gruel, uncle?

Uncle J.   No, I won't.   I can't eat anything now.

Dora *takes the dish from the room and returns without it*.

Uncle J.   Theodora!

Dora.   Sir.

Uncle J.   I'll try just a spoonful of that gruel before it gets cold

Dora.   Why, uncle, I threw it away.

Uncle J.   Threw my gruel away?

Dora.   Yes, uncle, you told me you didn't want it.

Uncle J.   I told you so?   Furies and fiddle strings!   You might know by this time that I didn't mean half I say.   Get me some more. If I hadn't been bedridden for more than a year I could go faster than you do.   Oh dear! to think I shall never walk again!

Dora.   Uncle Joseph, the doctor said yesterday that he really thought if you were to try you could walk as well as anybody.

Uncle J.   The doctor's a fool and you may tell him so with my compliments.

Dora.   I will, uncle, next time he comes.

Uncle J.   Theodora, if you do I'll disinherit you.

Dora.   Very well, uncle.   [*Leaves the room.*]

Uncle J. (*to himself*).   What can ail Dora?   I never saw her half as stupid.   She'd tell the doctor that.   Any half-witted simpleton might know better.

Dora *returns with the gruel*.

Dora.   There's your gruel, uncle, all smoking hot.

UNCLE J. Theodora, you'll have to feed me. This annoyance has weakened me dreadfully.

DORA. Yes, uncle. [*Commences to feed him.*]

UNCLE J. Stop! stop! it's hot! You're choking me! Stop, I say! Didn't I tell you to stop? Do you want to burn me to death? I don't believe there's an inch of skin left in my throat.

DORA. You told me yourself, uncle, that you don't mean half you say. How did I know that the gruel was really burning you?

UNCLE J. What's that smoke?

DORA. I think it is Mrs. Perkins putting some more wood on the kitchen fire.

UNCLE J. No it isn't. The house is on fire.

DORA (*rushes from the room screaming*). Fire! fire! fire! fire! help! murder! thieves! help! help!

UNCLE J. Oh! oh! fire! fire! oh, dear! oh, dear! oh! help! help! Will nobody come to help me out of the burning house? Oh, dear! do help quick! quick (*raps with his cane*) Come, come, come, now. Do come. [*Jumps up—Curtain falls.*]

SCENE V.

UNCLE JOSEPH *runs into the kitchen.*

MRS. P. Goodness! if here isn't master a'most scart to death?

UNCLE J. Where's the fire? Where's the fire?

MRS. P. There isn't any fire that I know of only in the stove here. It always smokes jest so when it is first kindled.

UNCLE J. Where did you see the fire, Dora?

DORA. I didn't see any fire, but you said the house was on fire, and I supposed it must be so. Do go back to bed, uncle; it was only a false alarm, you see.

UNCLE J. I won't go back. Theodora, I won't go back *to that bed to-day*.

DORA. But you are very sick, uncle, and this *excitement will surely* kill you. Do go back.

UNCLE J. No, I'm not so very sick, child.

DORA. Do you really mean it Uncle Joseph? Can you walk as well as ever?

UNCLE J. Yes, I can, Dode, I guess the scare limbered up my old stiffened limbs a little.

DORA. Well, then, uncle, let's go into the sitting-room. You need rest, come. [*They leave the stage.*]

MRS. P. (*alone*). Didn't I tell her it was only the hypo? It is a good thing something started him. The old man finds he can walk, after all. I b'leve Dora did it a purpose—the little trollop—I seen her a laughin' to herself. And this is how she cured him Wal, wal, she's cute, no mistake.

A FAMILY JAR.

CHARACTERS:

JOHN BROOKE	
MEG BROOKE	*His Wife*.
MR. SCOTT	
LOTTY	*A Servant*

SCENE I.

A room in MEG'S *house.* MEG, *arrayed in a dainty morning-dress, a bit of a muslin cap on her head, is engaged in putting the room to rights, and dusting.*

MEG. Yes! I am determined to be a model housekeeper! Every room shall always be in the most perfect order. No dust, no fly-specks, from one end of the house to the other. Dear John loves order so well! Bless his heart! What won't I do to please him? He shall find home a paradise. He shall always see me with a smiling face. No matter what happens while he is gone, or how much out of sorts I may feel, when I know it is time to expect him, I shall take care to look my prettiest, and have a kiss of welcome for him. He shall always find a good table, too. That is so important. He shall fare sumptuously every day; so that he will declare he never knew what good living was, when he had to depend on those vile restaurants.—Here he comes now, all ready to go down town.

Enter JOHN, *wearing a thin overcoat, hat in hand.*

JOHN. I am off, dear!

MEG. O, must you go so soon?

JOHN. Yes, dear. I ought to have gone ten minutes ago. How charming you look this morning! You don't find housekeeping a great bugbear, do you?

MEG. I guess I don't! For my part, I don't see what people mean by making such a talk about the difficulties of housekeeping. It is only fun to me. Perhaps it is because you are always so kind and considerate.

JOHN. Do you think so? Well, it is pleasant to hear you say so at any rate. Perhaps you may not always think so; for instance, when I might chance to meet a friend, and ask him home to dinner, and you know nothing about ——

MEG. Now, John, dear! did you ever come home and find me looking otherwise than you would have me look, should half a dozen friends come in unexpectedly? Or should you ever have been ashamed of our table since we were married?

JOHN. No, Meg. I must say you have surpassed my expectations in this respect. But I thought perhaps you might be shy at the idea of entertaining strangers, for fear everything on the table should not be "O. K."

MEG. My husband shall always feel free to bring a friend home whenever he likes. I shall always be prepared. There shall be no flurry, no scolding, no discomfort, but a neat house, a cheerful wife, and a good dinner. John, dear, never stop to ask my leave. Invite whom you please, and be sure of a welcome from me!

JOHN (*aside*). How charming to hear her talk thus! It is a blessed thing to have a superior wife! [*Aloud.*] I must go now. [*Giving her a parting salute.*] Shall I send home veal or mutton for dinner?

MEG. Beef to roast, dear, for to-day; and any vegetable you may happen to fancy. Would you like an oyster-soup, too? If so, stop in and order home a quart of oysters. Only a quart; that will be sufficient. O, something more! Have sent at once—at once remember!—a dozen or so of little jars, each holding about a pint. Our currants are all spoiling. I must make some into jelly this very day.

JOHN. All right. I'll remember. Beef—vegetables—oysters—and jelly-jars.

MEG. And be sure and have the little jars come at once!

JOHN. Yes. Good-by, dear!

MEG. Good-by! [*Throwing a kiss after him. Exit* JOHN.] Now I must finish dusting this room, and then I'll run up stairs and change my dress and put on a big calico apron. I must have that jelly on at once, so as to have it out of the way in season for dinner.

SCENE II.

MEG'S *kitchen in great disorder. On the table several little jelly-jars on a waiter, partly filled with currant juice. A kettle on the floor; another on the fire.* LOLLY *standing by the table, calmly eating bread-and-butter and currant juice.* MEG *sits sobbing dismally with her apron over her head.* SCOTT *is seen looking slyly through the window.*

JOHN (*rushing in*). My dearest girl, what is the matter?

MEG. O, John, I *am* so tired, and hot, and cross, and worried! I've been at it till I'm all worn out. Do come and help me, or I shall die! [*Throwing herself on* JOHN'S *breast.*]

JOHN. What worries you, my dear? Has anything dreadful happened?

MEG (*despairingly*). Yes.

JOHN. Tell me quick, then. Don't cry. I can bear anything better than that. Speak out, love! What is it?

MEG. The—jelly won't jell—and I don't know what to do!

JOHN (*laughing heartily*). Is that all? Fling it out of the window, and don't bother any more about it. I'll buy you quarts if you want it; but for heaven's sake don't have hysterics, for I've brought Jack Scott home to dinner, and—

MEG (*casting* JOHN *off, clasping her hands with a tragic gesture, and*

falling into a chair).   A man to dinner, and everything in a mess!
John Brooke, how *could* you do such a thing?

JOHN.   Hush, he's in the garden!   I forgot the confounded jelly;
but it can't be helped now.   [*Surveying the room with an anxious eye.*]

MEG (*petulantly*).   You ought to have sent word, or told me this
morning; and you ought to have remembered how busy I was!

JOHN.   I didn't know it this morning, and there was no time to
send word, for I met him on the way out.   I never thought of asking
leave, when you have always told me to do as I liked.   I never tried
it before, and hang me if I ever do again!   [*With an aggrieved air.*]

MEG.   I should hope not!   Take him away at once.   I can't see
him; and there isn't any dinner.

JOHN.   Well, I like that!   Where's the beef and vegetables I sent
home, and the pudding you promised?

MEG.   I had'nt time to cook anything; I meant to dine at mother's.
I'm sorry, but I was *so* busy.   [*Beginning to be in tears again.*]

JOHN.   It's a scrape, I acknowledge; but if you will lend me a
hand, we'll pull through, and have a good time yet.   Don't cry, dear,
but just exert yourself a bit, and knock us up something to eat.
We're both as hungry as hunters, so we sha'n't mind what it is.
Give us cold meat, and bread and cheese; we won't ask for *jelly.*

MEG (*touched by his joke, and losing patience*).   You must get yourself out of the scrape as best you can.   I'm too used up to "exert"
myself for anyone.   It's like a man, to propose a bone and vulgar
bread and cheese for company.   I won't have anything of the sort in
the house.   Take that Scott up to mother's, and tell him I'm away,
sick, dead—anything.   I won't see him, and you two can laugh at me
and my jelly as much as you like; you won't have anything else here
[*Defiantly.   Then, casting away her pinafore, she precipitately leaves the
room.*]

JOHN (*looking after her, and biting his lips with indignation.*)   It is'nt
fair to tell a man to bring folks home any time, with perfect freedom;
and when he takes you at your word, to flare up and blame him, and
leave him in the lurch to be laughed at or pitied.   No, by George, it

isn't! And Meg shall know it, too. But it won't do to stand here and talk, with Scott waiting outside there, hungry as a bear. Here, Lotty, straighten matters out a little. Throw away all your sweet stuff, and hide the pots.

LOTTY. Yes—sir.

JOHN. Now give us a clean table-cloth.

LOTTY. Yes—sir. [*John helps her adjust it on the table.*]

JOHN. So—that's right, isn't it?

LOTTY. Yes—sir.

JOHN. What on earth ails my feet? They stick to the floor as if they meant to grow there. [*Looks at the soles of his boots.*] Currant jelly, by jingo! [LOTTY *covers her mouth to suppress a laugh.*] What a mess to get a fellow into! Lotty, can't you get a dish-cloth—towel floor-rag—anything, to wipe up a little?

LOTTY. Yes—sir. [*Brings in a mop, and quickly passes it over the floor.* JOHN, *in the meantime, takes a newspaper out of his pocket, tears it, and wipes the jelly off the bottom of his boots.*]

JOHN. There! [*throwing the paper into the fire*] that will do! Now, what is there in the house to eat? Where do you keep the victuals? [LOTTY *opens the closet door.*]

LOTTY. Not much in there, sir.

JOHN. I'll warrant it! [*Takes out a cold bit of lamb; smells of it.*] That's eatable. Put that on.

LOTTY. Yes—sir.

JOHN (*taking out another plate with some once-carved bones and bits of ham on it*). Put that on.

LOTTY. Yes—sir.

JOHN. Here's some cold potatoes. Put them on.

LOTTY. Ye-es—sir.

JOHN. What's this?

LOTTY. Pudding-sauce.

JOHN. Put it on.

LOTTY. Sir?

JOHN (*impatiently*). Put it on!

LOTTY (*aside*). Well, I never!

JOHN (*taking out a covered dish and opening it*). Cheese. Put it on.

LOTTY. Yes—sir.

JOHN (*taking out a plate of broken bread*). Is this the best bread you have in the house?

LOTTY. Yes—sir.

JOHN. Put it on.

LOTTY (*aside*). O, mercy! what would Misses say if she only knew?

JOHN. Now we've got the royal feast spread; I must call in the invited guest.

LOTTY. Sir?

JOHN (*glancing at table.*) You don't suppose we are going to eat with our fingers, do you? Put on some plates, and knives and forks.

LOTTY. Yes—sir.

JOHN. Hang it all! [*Goes out and brings in* SCOTT.] Walk right in. [*Slapping his back.*] Make yourself at home. I am sorry I cannot have the pleasure of introducing you to my better half. The truth is—she—isn't well—has met with an accident. [LOTTY *struggles to suppress an explosive laugh.*]

SCOTT. I am sorry. Nothing serious, I hope?

JOHN. O—no; accidents will happen in the best of families, you know. [*Aside.*] Won't I give her a piece of my mind? [*Aloud.*] Mrs. Brooke is the most hospitable of hostesses,—always delighted to see her friends,—as she would be now, were it not for this unforeseen accident. [*Aside.*] Confound that jelly! [*Aloud.*] Here, take a bit of this lamb. It was delicious yesterday. Wife has a knack of giving such a relish. [*Aside.*] As if a *ton* of that sweet stuff could pay for this!

SCOTT. I declare, John, you wear the honors of a host well.

JOHN. Never happier in my life.—Bring in some cider!

LOTTY. Yes—sir.

JOHN. Wife's uncle sent her some very nice cider—pure article—just from the press.

SCOTT.   I am particularly **fond of cider.**   None of your lager beer, when I can get good cider!

LOTTY *returns with a jug.   She fills from it a small pitcher, which she then places on a table.*

JOHN.   Now some goblets.

LOTTY.   Yes—sir.

JOHN (*delightedly filling both goblets from the pitcher.*)   I am really glad we happened to have this nice cider in the house, since you are so fond of it.

SCOTT.   Thank you.   [*Raising the glass and looking through it.*] It is wonderfully clear.

JOHN (*clicking his goblet against* SCOTT's).   Here's to the health of the future Mrs. Scott!   [*They both drink, but commence at once to strangle and cough.*]

LOTTY (*throwing up her hands and screaming out*).   O mercy!   I got the wrong jug; I have given them *vinegar.*

SCENE III.

MEG's *parlor, containing sofa, chairs, rocking-chair and table.   Meg prettily dressed, enters with her work-basket, which she places on the table.*

MEG (*looking at the watch*).   Almost time for John to be here.   I don't care!   I'm not particularly anxious too see him!   He had no business to serve me so; he knew I was going to make jelly.   A queer time those horrid creatures must have had!   Lotty says John pulled out all the odds and ends he could find in the pantry—even to those bones I was to make a soup of.   What *would* mother say?   I know, I suppose.   She would say, "'Meg, dear, be the first to ask pardon, if you err."   I can't!   I won't!   He don't deserve it,—so there!—Hark! he's coming!   [*Takes out her work, rocks to and fro and begins to hum a song.   Enter* JOHN.]

JOHN (*aside*).   I was over-anxious about her making herself sick with crying.   Dignified as you please!   [*Walks leisurely to the sofa, and reclines upon it.*]   We are going to have a new moon, my dear.

MEG. I've no objection. [*A pause.*]

JOHN. I met your sister Jo down the street. She was in a great hurry about something.

MEG. That's nothing unusual. [*A pause.*]

JOHN. Do you know what day of the week Christmas occurs on, this year?

MEG. I presume the almanac will tell you.

JOHN *looks about abstractedly for a moment, and then with apparent indifference takes out his newspaper and reads it.* MEG *turns her back, and sews for dear life.*

MEG (*aside*). O dear! married life is very trying, and does need infinite patience as well as love, as mother says. [*Glances at* JOHN.] He looks tired. Poor John! Shall I be sorry for this? It *was* too bad to get angry with him this noon. [*Puts down her work and rises to her feet.*] Mother says, hasty words often pave the way for bitter sorrow and regret. I *will* be the first to say "Forgive me!" [*Goes slowly across the room, and stands at the end of the sofa, near* JOHN'S *head. He takes no notice of her.*] I *can't* give in!—This is our first misunderstanding; I'll do my part and have nothing to reproach myself with. [*Stoops, and kisses his forehead.* JOHN *seats her by his side in a moment.*]

JOHN. It was too bad to laugh at the poor little jelly jars! Forgive me, dear; I never will again.

MEG. Ha, ha! Do you think I believe you! By the way, John, how many courses did you have for dinner?

JOHN. So many that Scott said he had a right good time, and wants to come again.

MEG. Good! He must come! and I shall not be content till I write a note and invite him. [*Goes to a table and writes, then hands the note to* JOHN.] There; will that do?

JOHN (*reads*):

"Unfortunate occurrences having deprived me of the pleasure of meeting to-day my husband's old friend, will Mr. Scott favor us with his company to dine next Tuesday, and thus give happiness to   MEG BROOKE."

●—S. C.

JOHN.   That is like you, dear!   And I shall order for dinner?

MEG.   Oysters, ———

JOHN.   Oysters, ———

MEG.   Beef to roast, ———

JOHN.   Beef to roast, ———

MEG.   Vegetables, ———

JOHN.   Ah, yes!   Vegetables, ———

MEG.   But *not* jars for jelly, John!

JOHN (*apparently surprised*).   No!

MEG.   "No!"   You saucy fellow!   [*Boxing his ears.*]

JOHN.   I tell you what, Meg (*throwing his arm around her waist*), I should not object to having some—more—jars in the house, if we can have them filled with such sweets as these.   [*Kissing her.*]

MEG.   Are you sure they will *keep* well?

JOHN.   So sure that I sincerely hope (*taking* MEG'S *hand and looking to the audience*) family peace may be preserved in every FAMILY JAR.   LOUISA M. ALCOTT.

LITTLE RED RIDING-HOOD; OR, THE WICKED WOLF AND THE VIRTUOUS WOODCUTTER.

CHARACTERS:

JACK, *the woodcutter, who rescues* RED RIDING-HOOD *from the* WOLF, *quite by accident.*

THE WOLF, *a wicked wretch, who pays his* devours *to* LITTLE RED RIDING-HOOD, *but is defeated by his rival.*

DAME MARGERY, *mother of* LITTLE RED RIDING-HOOD, *a crusty* role, *and very ill-bred.*

LITTLE RED RIDING-HOOD, *a fascinating little pet, so lovely that you are not likely to see two such faces under a hood.*

THE FAIRY FELICIA, *a beneficent genius, versed in spells, and quite* au fay *in magic.*

GRANNY, *an invisible old girl, by kind permission of the Prompter.*

NOTE.—The dresses are easily enough contrived, with the exception of the Wolf. A rough shawl or a fur jacket will answer the purpose, and the head can be made with an animal mask, for sale at costumers' and other place in most cities.

The Butterfly in Scene II is affixed to wire held at the wings. The Prompter reads the part of Granny, standing close to the bed, in order to assist in getting rid of the Dummy when Wolf is supposed to eat it.

SCENE I.

The exterior of LITTLE RED RIDING-HOOD'S *Cottage. Enter* RED RIDING-HOOD'S MOTHER. *She runs about the stage looking for her child.*

MOTHER.   Red Riding-Hood!   Red Riding-Hood, I say!
Where can the little monkey hide away?
Red Riding-Hood! O dreary, dreary me!
    Provoking child, where ever can she be! [*Looks off on both sides.*]
She is a shocking disobedient child,
Enough to drive a loving mother wild;
But stay! where are the butter and the cake
That to her grandmother she has to take?

Fetches basket from cottage and shows cake and butter.

Here is the cake, and here's the butter, see!
The nicest cake and butter that could be.
These in the basket I will neatly lay,
A present to poor Granny to convey.
They are not tithes, though given to the wicker;

Puts them in basket.

Bless me, I wish the child were only quicker!
Red Riding-Hood, Red Riding-Hood!   Dear, dear!

Enter LITTLE RED RIDING-HOOD.

R. R.-H.   Here I am, ma.
MOTHER.   You wicked puss, come here!
Take this to Granny!   Poor old soul, she's ill;
Give her my love and these tidbits.

R. R.-H.   I will.

Won't it be nice ?   Through wood and field I'll walk,
And have with Jack, perhaps, a little talk.
Dear Jack !   At thought of him why quickly beat, heart?
Dear Jack ! he's no Jack-pudding, but a sweet-tart!
Won't I catch butterflies and gather flowers!

MOTHER.   Mind you don't dawdle and be gone for hours,
But go straight there and back again with speed,
And do not loiter in lane, wood, or mead,
Or else a great big wolf shall come to eat you ;
At any rate your loving mother'll beat you !

Threatens R. R.-H. *with stick.   Enter* JACK, *at back.*

JACK.   Where is Red Riding-Hood, my heart's delight?
La, there's her mother !   What a horrid fright !

MOTHER.   What are you doing here, you rascal Jack?
Be off, or I will hit your head a crack.   [*Strikes at him
but misses.*]

JACK.   Before your hits, ma'am, I prefer a miss ;

Bows to R. R.-H.

So blow for blow, I mean to blow a kiss.   [*Kisses hand to*
R. R.-H.]

MOTHER.   Kisses be blo—

JACK.   Hush! don't be coarse and low:
If you don't like my company, I'll go ;
Your words are violent, your temper quick,
So this young woodcutter will cut his stick.

He and R. R.-H. *exchange signs, blow kisses, etc.   Exit* JACK.

MOTHER (*to* R. R.-H.).   That spark is not your match, and you're to
blame.
To take de-light in such a paltry flame.
Now go ; and lose no time upon the road,
But hasten straight to Grandmother's abode.

R. R.-H.   I will not loiter, mother, by the way,
Nor go in search of butterflies astray.
Instead of picking flowers, my steps I'll pick,
And take the things to Granny, who is sick.
Good by, dear mother.

MOTHER (*kisses her*).   There, my dear, good by.

R. R.-H.   See how obedient to your word I fly!

MOTHER.   A one-horse fly! What nonsense you do talk!
You have no wings, and so of course must walk.
You go afoot. How now, miss? Wherefore smile?

R. R.-H.   Why go afoot? I've got to go a mile;
That was the reason, mother, why I smiled.

MOTHER.   That joke's so far-fetched, that it's very miled.   [*Exeunt.*

SCENE II.

A Forest Glade.   Enter RED RIDING-HOOD.

R. R.-H   How nice the wood is, with its cool green shade!
I must sit down and rest here, I'm afraid;
Though mother would declare I'm only lazy.
I'm very tired and weary.   [*Yawns, then sees flower
          starts.*]   Lawk! a daisy!   [*Picks flowers.*]
It can't be wrong some pretty flowers to pull;
With them I'll fill my little apron full,
And take to please my poor old granny's eye.

          Butterfly flies across the stage.

O, isn't that a lovely butterfly?   [*Runs after it.*]
Stop, little butterfly, a moment, do.

 Tries to catch it, and runs into the arms of JACK, *who enters.*

    I've caught it.

JACK.   Beg your pardon, I've caught you.   [*Kisses her.*]

R. R.-H.   Don't you be rude, sir! Fie, why treat me thus!

JACK.   You thought to take a fly, I took a bus.
I love you, pretty maid! Suppose we say
That we'll be married? Just you fix the day. [*Embraces her.*

R. R.-H.   You're very pressing, sir! Well, let me see:
            Next Wednesday a wedding's day shall be.

Jack.   An earlier date far better, dear, will do;
            Say, why not Tuesday as the day for two?
            Another kiss!

R. R.-H.   A kiss? O dear me, no!
            Farewell. To poor old Granny's I must go,
            For mother has commanded me to take
            The poor old soul some butter and a cake.

Jack.   I'm off to work, then.

R. R.-H.   Whither go you, pray?

Jack.   I'm not quite sure, but mean to axe my way.   [*Exit*

R. R.-H.   Now I must hurry off to Granny.

Fairy *appears*.

                                    Law!
            How lovely! such a sight I never saw.

Fairy.   I am a fairy, and your friend, my dear;
            You'll need my aid, for there is danger near.
            Your disobedience to your mother's will
            Has given bad fairies power to work you ill.

R. R.-H.   Thanks, beauteous fairy. But no harm I meant,
            And of my disobedience much repent.

Fairy.   I know it, and will therefore prove your friend;
            You shall o'ercome your troubles in the end.
            Remember when your case my help demands,
            You've naught to do save simply clap your hands.

Exit Fairy.

R. R.-H.   How very sorry I am now that I
            Was disobedient: let the time slip by,
            Neglected Granny and my mother's words,
            To gather flowers and list to singing birds,
            To hunt the butterflies. 'Twas wrong, I fear—
            But, goodness gracious me, what have we here?

Enter WOLF.

WOLF.   O, what a very pretty little girl!
          Such rosy cheeks, such hair, so nice in curl!
 (*Aside*.) As tender as a chicken, too, I'll lay;
          One doesn't get such tidbits every day.
To R. R.-H.) What brings you wandering in the wood like **this**,
          And whither are you going, pretty miss?

R. R.-H.   I'm bound for Granny's cottage, but I fear
          I've strayed from the right path in coming here.
          I'm taking her a currant-cake and butter;
          So nice, their excellence no tongue can utter.

WOLF (*aside*). However excellent, I'll bet I lick it;
          As to the cake, I'll gobble pretty quick it.
To H. R.-H.) And where does Granny live?

R. R.-H.   Not far from **this**;
          It's near the river.

WOLF (*pointing off*). Then, my little miss,
          Along that path you have but to repair,
          And very shortly you will find you're there.

R. R. H.   O, thank you; now I'll go.   [*Exit*

WOLF   And I'll be bound
          You'll find that same short cut a long way round.
          The nearest road to the cottage take,
          And of old Granny I short work will make,
          And then I'll gobble *you* up, little dear.
          I didn't like to try and eat you here;
          You might object to it—some people do—
          And scream and cry, and make a hubbuboo;
          And there's a woodcutter, I know, hard by,
          From whose quick hatchet quick-catch-it should **I**!
          Here goes to bolt old Granny without flummery,
          A spring—and then one swallow shall be summery!
                              [*Exit*.

SCENE III.

Interior of GRANDMOTHER'S *cottage. On the right hand, close to the wing, a bed with a dummy in it with a large nightcap. WOLF is heard knocking.*

GRANNY (*spoken from the wing close by the bed*).   Who's there?

WOLF (*imitating* R. R.-H.).   Your little grandchild, Granny dear

GRANNY.   That child has got a shocking cold, that's clear.
            Some carelessness—she's got her feet wet through
            With running in the rain or heavy dew,
            Perhaps without her bonnet; and, of course,
            The little donkey is a little hoarse.
            Her words she used not croakingly to utter—
            What do you want?

WOLF.   I've brought you cake and butter,
            But can't come in, the door my strength defies.

GRANNY.   Pull at the bobbin, and the latch will rise.

                         Enter WOLF.

GRANNY.   How are you, little darling?

WOLF.   Darling! Pooh!
            You didn't bolt your door, so I'll bolt you!

GRANNY.   O, mercy! murder! what is this I see?
            Some frightful spectre must the monster be!

WOLF.   Don't make a noise, for you're a hopeless hobble in;
            I'm not a ghost, but soon shall be a gobble-in'!

WOLF *flings himself on the bed; shrieks and growls are heard. The dummy is removed without the audience being able to see it, as WOLF is in front of it.*

WOLF (*coming down*).   Yahen! yahen! yahen! yahen! yahen!
            I've finished her ere she could angry be with me.
            I didn't give her time to disagree with me.
            Now for a night-gown (*takes one*) and a night-cap (*takes
                one*).   Good!   [*Puts them on.*]
            How do I look as Grandma Riding-Hood?

Gets into bed and covers himself up.   A knock is heard at the door

WOLF (*imitating* GRANNY'S *voice*).   Who's there?

R. R.-H.   Your little grandchild, Granny dear;
           I have a cake and butter for you here.

WOLF.   Pull at the bobbin and the latch will **rise**.

Enter R. R.-H.

R. R.-H.   Good morning, Granny! here are the supplies.

Sets down basket.

WOLF.   Good morning, dear, come sit beside my bed.
           I'm very bad indeed, child, in my head.

R. R.-H. *sits on the side of bed.*

R. R.-H.   Why, Granny, what big ears you've got?
WOLF.   My dear,
           That is that Granny may the better hear.

R. R.-H.   And, Granny, what big eyes you've got!
WOLF.   Dear me!
           That is that Granny may the better see.

R. R.-H.   Then, Granny, what big teeth you've got?   O, la!

WOLF.   To eat you up with all the better. [*Springs out of bed
           and strikes an attitude.*]   Ha!

R. R.-H. *screams, and runs away;* WOLF *pursues her round the table.*
Enter JACK.

JACK.   As I was passing by, I just dropt in. [*To* WOLF.]   Shall
           I drop into you?

WOLF.   O, pray begin!

JACK.   You hideous brute, your wicked game I'll stop.

Hits WOLF *with axe.*

           How do you like that, monster?
WOLF.   That's first chop!

JACK.   That isn't all,—another chop to follow!

Strikes him again.   They struggle. WOLF *falls with a loud cry*
           Don't holloa, sir!

WOLF.   I must,—I'm beaten hollow;
          You've felled me to the earth.

JACK.   Yes, I'm the feller!
          I'll beat you black and blue.

WOLF (*aside*),   Then I'll turn yeller!

*Goes into convulsions, shrieks, and feigns to be dead.   JACK flings down
          axe, and embraces R. R.-H.*

R. R.-H.   You've saved my life, dear Jack!   What can I do
          To show my love and gratitude to you?

JACK.   Sweetest Red Riding-Hood, say you'll be mine,
          To jine our hands the parson I'll enjine.

          WOLF *creeps behind them, and secures the axe.*

WOLF (*leaping up*)   That en-gine won't assist you, tender pair;

          Snatches up R. R.-H. *with one arm, brandishing axe.*

          If that's your line, why I shall raise the fare.

JACK.   He's got the axe—O, here's a nice quandary!

R. R.-H. (*claps hands*).   You'll raise the fare?   Then I will raise the
                    fairy!

          FAIRY *appears at the back.   Enter* R. R.-H.'s MOTHER.

MOTHER.   You wicked child, where have you been?   Oho!
          You're listening to the *shoot* of that young beau!
          But I'll forbid it, and I'll have my way.

          FAIRY *comes forward.*

FAIRY.   Excuse me, but your orders I gainsay.

MOTHER.   Who are you, madam, I should like to ask?

FAIRY.   I am the Fairy of the Wood, whose task
          It is to aid the weak against the strong,
          And set things right when they are going wrong.
          You, Master Wolf, please keep that hatchet ready;
          For that sad jest of eating the old lady,
          You shall die, jester, by that very tool!
          Dame Margery, you have acted like a fool.

MOTHER.	Good Mistress Fairy, why, what have I done?
FAIRY.	Jack is no peasant, but a prince's son,
	Stolen from the crib by an old cribbing gypsy,
	When he was little and his nurse was tipsy.
MOTHER.	You don't say!
JACK.	I a prince!
R. R.-H.	Good gracious, mother!
	Is he that 'ere?
FAIRY.	He's that heir, and no other.
	Your mother won't reject his house and lands,
	Though she did him; so here I join your hands,
	With blessings, from the Fairy of the Wood,
	On brave Prince Jack and fair Red Riding-Hood.

THOMAS HOOD.

CRAB VILLAGE LYCEUM.

CHARACTERS:

THE PRESIDENT, MR. HOBBS, MR. STUBBS, MR. SNUBBS, MR. TANTRUM, MR. SLOW, MR. SURE, MR. TRIPP, MR. STUMP, MR. PARLEY, MR. FLAREUP.

MR. HOBBS. Mr. President, the subjec' afore the meetin' for debate this evenin' is Newspapers; and I rise to say that I take t'other side.

Mr. STUBBS (*springing to his feet*). Mr. President, I'd like to ask what the speaker means by *t'other side*.

Mr. HOBBS. By t'other side I mean—t'other side; and that's the side, of course, that's opposed to *t'other side*.

Mr. STUBBS. Mr. President: If by *t'other side* the speaker intends to cast any insinuations upon the side that I am on, allow me, Mr. President, to say that his remark is unparliamentary and untrue.

Mr. SNUBBS. Mr. President: If the gentlemen who have begun the debate will come to the p'int,—that is, if they have any p'int to come to,—and not talk round the p'int, I'll be most obleeged; if not, I shall make it a p'int to object: and I'll say, further, that if they hain't got any p'int to come to, they'd better app'int some other speakers, and not disapp'int the meeting.

Mr. TANTRUM.   Mr. President: I hope speakers will not be allowed to interrupt speakers in this way.   For if speakers are to be permitted to interrupt speakers in this manner, then there is an end of free speech, and speakers may as well keep their seats.   No gag-laws, Mr. President.   If I understood Mr. Snubbs correctly, Mr. Snubbs called upon Mr. Stubbs and Mr. Hobbs to come to the p'int; and I will say that when Mr. Snubbs calls upon Mr. Stubbs or Mr. Hobbs to come to the p'int, Mr. Snubbs requires more of Mr. Stubbs and Mr. Hobbs than Mr. Stubbs himself can do.   For he never can come to the p'int as long as he remains so blunt.

Mr. SLOW.   Mr. President,—Mister—President: The subject before this meeting, for debate this evening, as one of the previous speakers has so well observed, is the subject of Newspapers; *be they a cuss, or be they a blessin'?*   Mr. President, I agree with the previous speaker.

Mr. SNUBBS, Mr. STUBBS, Mr. HOBBS *and* Mr. SURE *all spring to their feet at once, shouting,* "Mr. PRESIDENT! Mr. PRESIDENT!"

THE PRESIDENT (*rapping on his desk*).   Order! order! Mr. Sure has the floor.

Mr. SURE.   Mr. President: When I started to come to the meetin' this evenin', my marm she called me back, and says she, "Amy," says she,—for she mos' gen'ly allus calls me Amy, though my name's Amos, named arter my uncle Amos.   I guess most of the members present knowed my uncle Amos; and, though I do say it, in the words of Milton,—

> "Take him altogether
> We never shall look upon his likeness agin."

But as I was a-goin' to say, she called me back, and says she, "Amy," says she, "what's the debate on to this evenin'?" says she.

And when I said Noospapers, says she, "Noospapers," says she,— "noospapers; that's a good subjec' for debatin' on to," says she. "And now, Amy," says she, "don't forgit that your father never took a noospaper in his life, and he allus got along without 'em, till he was run over by the railroad, and both legs broke, and they're all a useless expense," says she; "and if anybody claims they're necessary, you jest up and ax 'em, What did Adam and Eve, what did Noar, what did the Patriarchs do without noospapers?" says she. And now I ax that question. Mr. President, I stand here, and ax, What's the good o' noospapers, which our forefathers got along without 'em, and never heard of sich a thing? Mr. President!

Mr. TRIPP. Mr. President and Gentlemen. When a gentleman comes into this lyceum, and carries into the debate some remark which his *marm* made to him just previously to his leaving the parental domicile, and he makes that remark his argyment, his sole argyment, in the discussion, Mr. President, we naturally infer that he has no ideas of his own on the subject, and that he had better have sent his marm in his place, while he stayed to home to tend the baby. For my part, I stand up for the newspapers; and beg to suggest, that if the father of the last speaker *had* taken a paper, and if the last speaker had been brought up to *read* that paper, we should have been saved the humiliating spectacle, Mr. President, of a young man coming here without a notion of his own in his addled brains, to tell us what his *marm* told him to say!

Mr. STUMP. Mr. President: Newspapers is a cuss. Takin' newspapers is money throwed away; and readin' newspapers is time throwed away. Better be doin' suthin useful,—choppin' wood or darnin' stockin's. I knowed a man once that was allus a master-hand to be allus forever a readin' a newspaper; and that man was took up for sheep-stealin'; and 't was proved agin' him,—proved agin' him, Mr. President, that's what comes from readin' newspapers. Newspapers is a cuss.

THE PRESIDENT. If Mr. Snipe is present, we should be glad to hear from him on this momenchewous question.

Mr. PARLEY.   I see Neighbor Snipe this mornin', and he told me to tell the meetin' that his hoss wa'n't shod, and not bein' able to git his hoss shod, or to git a hoss, he found it impossible to 'tend the meetin'.   He wished me partic'lar to mention to the meetin' that the man that had been in the habit of shoein' his hoss was off on a spree, and so could *not* shoe his hoss, and, his hoss not bein' shod, he could not 'tend the meetin'.   He wished me partic'lar to state to the meetin', that, as his hoss was not shod, he could not 'tend the meetin'. His hoss not bein' shod, he could not 'tend the meetin'.

Mr. FLAREUP.   Mr. President: I wish friends in the fore part of the meeting would speak up, so that friends in the back part of the meeting could hear what's going on in the front part of the meeting. It is almost impossible for friends in the back part of the meeting to hear what's going on in the front part of the meeting.   Friends in the back part of the meeting feel as much interest as friends in the front part of the meeting ; and it is highly necessary that friends in the fore part of the meeting should speak up, so that friends in the back part of the meeting can hear what friends in the fore part of the meeting have to say.   And, therefore, I say that if friends in the fore part of the meeting would speak up, so that we setting in the back part of the meeting could hear what's going on in the front part of the meeting, it would be very satisfactory to friends in the back part of the meeting.

Mr. HOBBS.   As it's gittin' some late, and as Mr. Snipe is not present, and as a question of this natur' hadn't oughter be decided in a hurry, I move that this meetin' do now adjourn over to the next meetin' on Tuesday evenin' next.

Mr. STUBBS.   Second the motion.

THE PRESIDENT.   All them that's in favor of the motion to adjourn, please signify it by saying "Aye."

ALL BUT Mr. SNUBBS.   Aye!

THE PRESIDENT.   Contrary-minded, "No."

Mr. SNUBBS.   No!

THE PRESIDENT.   It's a vote.   This meeting is now adjourned.

AFTER SCHOOL, WHAT.

CHARACTERS:

LOUISE EARNEST; KATE SPANGLE; MADGE FLYAWAY; LIZZIE HELP-
FUL; SUSAN EASY; MISS LESLIE, *a teacher;* LITTLE GIRL.

SCENE, *a schoolroom.* PRESENT, LOUISE and KATE.

LOUISE. I say, Kate! what are you going to do when you leave school?

KATE. What am I going to do? Why, what's put that into your head?

LOUISE. It seems to me the most natural question in the world Here we are in the last half-quarter of a four years' course. A few more weeks, and we shall be scattered,—I was going to add, as my grandmother would have done, "one to his farm, and another to his merchandise." I wish I could say it!

KATE. Ha, ha, ha! That sounds well! You wish we were going to be farmers and merchants?

LOUISE. No, I don't mean that, literally; but I wish the spirit of it were true.

MADGE (*entering*). What's that you wish were true?

KATE. Good, Madge! I'm glad you're here. Come and sit down and hear what our future class-poet is singing about.

LOUISE. None of your nonsense, Kate! I'm in dead earnest; I mean every word I say; I can't say half I feel on the subject!

MADGE. What's up now? More fun? I am in for that! Was just wishing I could hear of some good news to drive dull care away.

KATE. Anything but fun. We are going to have a sermon. We have already had the text.

LOUISE. I'll tell you, Madge: I have been turning it over in my mind lately, how we girls are going to employ our time when we get through school. You know I have four brothers—

MADGE. Yes, I know that.

KATE. Of course! Madge always finds out, somehow or other

how many brothers any of us girls have. But go on with **your story,** Louise. I'll try to hold my tongue for five seconds.

LOUISE. How many seconds?

KATE *puts her fingers on her lips, and holds up five fingers, trying to look prim and sober.*

LOUISE. As I was saying, I have four brothers, who are all studying; and when we are at home together at vacation, I hear them discussing with the utmost eagerness what each shall do in life. Now, I have been with my brothers so much all my life, sharing their sports, in-doors and out, that I feel quite out in the cold when they get to talking about their future. I must say I wasn't much flattered the other day when I heard Will say, "What a bother it is, trying to find the right thing to do! Now, girls don't have such a time. All they have to think of when they leave school is, what shall be the color of their next dress."

KATE. I hope you don't object to a girl's giving attention to her dress. [*Looking over her shoulder with satisfaction at her own showy, well-fitting basque.*]

LOUISE. O no! of course not. But dress is not everything.

KATE. Dress is a good deal, let me tell you that! I'll wager I could make a better impression on your brothers, or any other young gentlemen, if I had on a stylish dress.

MADGE. That's so.

LOUISE. I wouldn't give a fig for any man who judged a girl by her dress alone!

MADGE. Nor I. One of the jolliest times I ever had in my life— when we were at the beach, you know—was one day when I had gone with Hal and Herbert on a fishing-scrape; had on a short dress, jacket to match, big rubber boots, and a great sun-hat that looked like a Chinese umbrella. *You,* Kate, wouldn't dare to go in such a rig.

LOUISE. I don't see anything particularly jolly in that.

KATE. Ah! she don't tell the whole story. Some of Hal's college friends came along—where's my fan?—only half a dozen, I believe;

GETTING TOO BIG TO KISS.

"Oh, no, no, no, no, sir! Allow me to pass;
Oh, no, a kiss is more than I dare:—
That game's out of fashion (I'm sorry, alas!)
You needn't look cross as a bear."

NOBODY'S CHILD
(Suggestion for Tableau)

"All day I wander to and fro
Hungry and shivering and nowhere to go
Oh! Why does the wind blow upon me so wild?
Is it because I'm nobody's child?"

three out of the six were—where's my smelling-bottle?—mortally wounded by Cupid's darts.

MADGE. How absurd you are, Kate!

KATE. It is the solemn truth! [*Looking very wise.*] One will never be seen on this mundane sphere again. The other two are still lingering along, but these (MADGE *gets up and tries to stuff her handkerchief in* KATE'S *mouth*) will soon be (*struggling with* MADGE) no more. Their epitaph will be—" Died of—a big pair of rubber boots!" [*The girls all laugh.*]

LOUISE. O Kate, you always remind me of a champagne bottle—full of sparkle and effervescence. But, seriously, there is something quite captivating in seeing a girl brave the elements in pursuit of health and fun. Suppose Madge had worn a long trail down over the rocks and into the fishing-wherry; don't you believe those same fellows would have laughed at her? My brothers would.

MADGE. I don't care that (*snapping her fingers*) whether a man laughs at me or not! When I'm in for a good time, don't bring me any of your trails and flounces! I hate long dresses, unless I am off for a horseback ride; and even then I wish I could cut off about so much (*measuring half a yard with her hands*).

SUSAN *enters.*

LOUISE. We are wandering from our subject somewhat. Here comes Susan Easy; let's ask her opinion. Susan, what are you going to do when you leave school?

SUSAN. Do? I'm sure I don't know—never asked myself. I suppose I shall do as other girls do: stay at home, when I am not away visiting; read, and write to my friends; practice a little; go to the opera. Won't it be jolly to have no more compositions to write?

KATE. I don't dread compositions very much.

SUSAN. You don't. They are the bugbear of my life.

MADGE. Louise, you have made me a little curious. I want to know what you are going to do.

LOUISE. That is just what I don't know. Wish from the bottom of my heart, I did.

10—S. C.

KATE. How absurd you are, Louise. You know I am crazy to have you go to Washington with me and spend the winter.

LOUISE. Yes, you would be very proud of me and my gay outfit of three or four dresses, wouldn't you, Kate?—you, with your splendid wardrobe, fresh from Paris. Say, Kate, be honest, and tell me if you should look forward now with quite so much zest to a winter in Washington, if you were to have no elegant dresses to display? Let me see; how many dozen have you ordered from Paris?

KATE (*a little touched*). I won't tell you, because you have hurt me. Just as if I should stop to ask how many yards of silk or cashmere you had in your trunk, if I could only have your own dear self!

LOUISE. Good! good! I am glad I have brought you to the point at last. You have acknowledged now that dress is not everything.

MADGE. Yes, she has owned up handsomely.

SUSAN (*to* LOUISE). You are one of the queerest girls I ever knew. Guess *I* shouldn't have to be asked twice to spend the winter in Washington!

LOUISE. I should enjoy going there,—hope I shall sometime; but I have a question or two to settle first. I can't enjoy myself anywhere till I know what I ought to do, when we leave these dear rooms. Kate, you don't suspect it, but I am quite as much exercised about you as about myself. Now, you have splendid talents. [KATE *bows mockingly*.] Your father has spent a small fortune on your education. It is a wicked shame for you to be so indifferent as to what you ought to do with your acquirements. You'll never rest content to simply dress and flirt; you know you won't.

SUSAN. Perhaps she'll get married.

LOUISE. That's all true. I hope she will some time. But in the meanwhile what is she to do, to think of? I don't know why girls should sit down and wait for marriage any more than their brothers. Any sensible man would think better of a girl if she exercised her faculties in some way helpful to society, than if she let them die out for want of use.

MADGE. So I say. Here comes Lizzie Helpful. She never talks much with us girls. I don't like to ask her about herself.

LIZZIE enters.

LOUISE. I had just as lief. I will be thankful to any one to show me the truth. Lizzie, we are talking about what we shall do when we leave school. What are you going to do? Are you anxious to have school close?

LIZZIE. Were I to consult my inclinations, I might stay here and study always; but I have others beside myself to think of. Perhaps you do not know that I have lost my father. My mother's income is small. I have several brothers and sisters younger than myself. Of course I must support myself and help support them. I am in hopes to help one of my brothers through college.

SUSAN. O dear! what a life of drudgery. Don't you *hate* to teach?

LIZZIE. Not at all. At least I do not since I hope to accomplish so much by it. I should be very glad if I could be sure of a paying school as soon as I leave here. My little sisters might come to me to be taught, and this would relieve mother of a great deal of anxiety on their account. They are bright, wide-awake girls, and mother could never afford to spend as much for their education as she has for mine.

LOUISE (*extending her hand to* LIZZIE). You are a lucky girl. I envy you. I wish every one of us could be as worthy of a diploma as you are.

Miss LESLIE (*enters, smiling*). Girls, I hope you will forgive me; but being in the next room, and the door being open, I could not avoid hearing your conversation; and I assure you the most of it has given me pleasure. You were speaking of Lizzie Helpful just now, and I wanted to call your attention to one fact that you may not have noticed. As Lizzie has had an object in studying, an aim in life, she has never been so perplexed by the difficulties in her four years' course as some of you have. Compositions, for instance, were at first quite distasteful to her, as was algebra; but she said to herself, I must become acquainted with these studies, **or I cannot teach them to others.** Hence she readily overcame her dislike to them.

I hope you will never forget your talk of to-day, girls. Think it over, and get some good out of it. I could have no greater happiness than to be sure my pupils will all make the highest use of what they have learned here. I hope to hear some day that Kate is an authoress,—writing books that will do good in the world.

KATE (*eagerly*). Do you think I ever could?

MISS L. Madge will, I trust, teach gymnastics, and give lessons in hygiene. Susan will, I am sure, be a good little housekeeper for her mother, and keep her father's accounts. You are very quick at figures (*to* SUSAN).

LOUISE (*rising*). And I?

MISS L. (*putting her hand on* LOUISE'S *head and thinking a moment*.) For you, dear child, I cannot seem to mark out a course. But you are thoroughly in earnest as to what is your duty. Heaven gives to those who seek. There will be a way of usefulness opened to you, I have no doubt.

A little girl enters bringing a note to MISS L., *who takes it and reads it to herself.*

MISS L. (*smiling*). This is a note that will interest you, girls. [*Reads.*]

"DEAR MISS LESLIE:—We are making preparations to leave for Europe, with our little daughters. I am exceedingly anxious to find a young lady to accompany us who shall be at once companionable to my wife, and competent to educate my little girls. She must be earnest and practical, desirous not only to *be* good, but to *do* good. If you know of any such young lady among your pupils who would like the situation, please answer by return mail, and oblige,

"Yours truly,
"HENRY B. CLAFLIN."

KATE. Mr. Claflin! I know him well. He has one of the most delightful families I ever met. I shouldn't object to travelling to Europe with them myself.

MADGE. I don't know who would.

SUSAN. I am dying to go to Europe.

Miss L. Louise, you have not had to wait very long for a chance to make yourself useful. I feel that this opportunity belongs to you, if you will take it.

Louise. I should like to go, above all things. I will write to my parents at once. [*Bell rings.*]

Kate. There is the bell for recitation.

Madge. Yes, we must hurry, or we shall all be late. [*Exeunt.*

FOX AND GEESE.

CHARACTERS { MOTHER GOOSE,
TWO YOUNG GEESE,
FOX.

BACKGROUND—*Brown muslin curtain.*
COSTUME—*Full white muslin cloaks with hoods. Yellow stockings.*
MOTHER GOOSE *in the chair. Could be dressed as in the engraving.*

MOTHER GOOSE.

COME, children dear, and listen to me,
   I'm feeble and old, as you can see,
   And soon away from this world of woe,
Your poor, old mother must go, go, go! [*Shakes her head.*]
Now, when I am gone, you must not fret,
Nor my good advice must you e'er forget.
Young geese are silly, and the fox is sly, [*Enter Fox unseen.*]
Remember that when you pass him by. [*Shakes her fingers.*]
And, children dear, whatever you do,
Never listen to him when he speaks to you!
And stay you at home when the hour is late,
Or sad, sad indeed will be your fate.
Young geese are silly, and the fox is sly,
Remember that when I die, die, die! [*Young geese kneel beside her.*]

FIRST YOUNG GOOSE.

Oh, mother dear, we will e'er be true,
When the fox is near we will think of you.

SECOND YOUNG GOOSE.

And though we may believe he is nice,
We'll be sure to remember your good advice;
And chance we to meet him, whenever the day,
We'll turn our faces the other way.

BOTH YOUNG GEESE (*in chorus*).

And when night comes we will never roam,
But think of the sly fox, and stay at home.

[*Rise hand in hand and repeat.*]

MOTHER GOOSE.

Young geese are silly, and the fox is sly,
Remember that when I die, die, die! [*Exit.*

SCENE II.

FIRST YOUNG GOOSE.

Come, take a walk, come, sister dear,
See! overhead the moon shines clear;
And, if our way the fox should pass,
We'll hide us down in some thick grass;
And, when he's gone, we'll hasten home—
Don't be a coward, sister, come!

SECOND YOUNG GOOSE.

Oh, sister dear, I should love to go;
But he, the old fox, is sly, you know.

FIRST YOUNG GOOSE.

What if he is! we are not afraid;
We'll show him that we geese are made
Of something more than feathers. Come!
We'll go not very fa from home.

They walk back and orth, hand in hand—meet Fox face to face. **Fox**
in brown fur cloak and hood.

MOTHER GOOSE.

Fox.

Good evening, oh, good evening! How d'ye do?
Two charming little maids like you
Should never walk alone.
I see, my dears, you're really quite afraid of me.
I'm not a handsome fellow, that I own,
And if you bid me, I'll go my way alone.
But come, my dears, I know you will—
Come walk with me to yonder moonlit hill;
I'll show you where the vine's rich clusters grow;
And you shall feast upon them—will you go?
  [*Aside.*]
I ask these silly geese on grapes to sup,
But when I get them safe, *I'll* eat *them* up!
                    [*Geese walk off, hand in hand, with Fox.*]

Scene III.

A pen made with chairs, Young Geese kneeling within.

Young Geese (*in chorus*).

Oh, please let us out, kind sir, please do,
And whatever you ask we will do for you.   [*Repeat.*]

Fox (*with contempt*).

What! let you out, now that I've got you in;
Why, my little dears, that would be a sin?
If you had been to your mother true,
You'd have shunned the trap I laid for you.
But now you are here, please don't blame me,
It's all your own fault, as you can see.
Young geese are silly, and the fox is sly,
Did you think of that when I passed you by?
And you listened to me when I spoke to you,
Is that what your mother advised you to do?

Oh, no! my dears, you may cackle and squeal,
But you're here to make me a luscious meal.
Good sense is but folly when it comes too late!
And a goose must expect but a goose's fate!
So, to-night you may sup on regret and tears,
To-morrow (*smacks his lips*)—good-night, pleasant dreams, my pretty
  dears!
 [*Aside.*]
I might have said more, but what's the use,
Of talking good sense to a silly young goose;
Young geese *will be* silly, and the fox is sly,
Remember that, kind friends, good-bye! good-bye!   ANNA M. FORD.

PAT ANSWERS THE ADVERTISEMENT.
[FOR TWO MALES.]

SCENE.—MR. PARKER, *seated at desk. Knock is heard. Enter* PATRICK.

PAT. Good-marnin', sorr! Oi come to say about the adv*ertise*-
ment. Oi think Oi'm jest the man fer the place.

 MR. PARKER. Oh! you do, eh?

 P. Oi do that.

 MR. P. What might your name be?

 P. Pathrick O'Rafferty. Handsome Pat, at your service.

 MR. P. Handsome Pat! Do you consider that a recommendation?

 P. It ginerally is wid the gurrls.

 MR. P. With the girls? Perhaps. But you won't have much to
do with girls here; we don't keep any.

 P. So much the bether. They're allus expectin' attintions; a
kiss behint the panthry dure, an' sich loike.

 MR. P. You won't be troubled that way here. Now, what can
you do?

 P. Phwat kin Oi do? Ask that o' me, Pat O'Rafferty, the
chrame av the b'yes, the pride o' the gurris. Phwat can't Oi do?

 MR. P. (*impatiently.*) What no Irishman can do—give a straight
answer.

P.   Indade, an' can't Oi?   Jest ask me the question p'int blank, an' see ef I can't answer it.

Mr. P.   I think I asked it plainly enough.   What can you do?

P.   Annythin'; annythin' at all.   It's glad Oi'll be to setthel down fer a toime, afther roving the worrld around these tin years.

Mr. P.   If you are such a rover, I fear you won't settle down for long.

P.   Faix, an' Oi'll hev to onc't Oi'm toied.

Mr. P. (*aside*.)   Tied!   I believe the man is crazy.   But I must have help of some kind, and he looks strong.   [*Aloud*.]   I suppose you can milk, tend the horses, plow, etc.?

P. (*ruefully*.)   W'u'd Oi hev to do all thim things?

Mr. P.   Why, yes.   What did you expect to do?

P.   Oi moight millk an' luk afther the chickens.   Oi don't think Oi'm sthrong enuf to plow.

Mr. P. (*aside*.)   Lazy.   [*Aloud*.]   You look strong enough to do most anything.

P.   Yis, Oi luk sthrong, but Oi've a crick in me back as won't let me do anny heavy worrk.

Mr. P.   Then I don't think you will suit me.

P.   Oi'm sorry, sorr, but if she's suited it won't make no difference.

Mr. P. (*aside*.)   The man is surely crazy.   [*Aloud*.]   She?   Who are you talking about?

P.   The young leddy, to be sure.

Mr. P.   Young lady?   What young lady?

P.   Her as advertised.

Mr. P.   As advertised?   I think you have made a mistake, and got into the wrong place.

P.   Isn't this Mr. Parker's, t'ree miles nort' o' Lynn?

Mr. P.   It is.

P.   Well, thin, this is the place, fur that's where the adver*tise*ment said.   She's your da'ther, I suppose.

Mr. P.   My daughter?   I have no daughter.   What *are* you driving at?

P.   No da'ther?   Beloike she's your sisther then.

Mr. P. "She" again. Please explain yourself. What did you come here for?

P. To answer the adver*tise*ment, sure.

Mr. P. I don't think you will suit as I said before, so we may as well close this interview. I want a man to work.

P. It don't matther phwat *ye* want, it's the leddy herself as Oi want to see. I moight suit her if Oi didn't ye.

Mr. P. Man alive! What *are* you driving at? I advertised for a man to work on my place. Now, *what* has any woman to do with it?

P. Yez didn't think all this toime as Oi was lukin' fur a place to wurrk, did yez? Not much! That ain't in moi loine.

Mr. P. Then what the dickens did you come here for?

P. I come to see the young leddy as advertised for a noice young fellar: object matrimony.

Mr. P. There is no such person here. There is no woman here but my sister.

P. Perhaps she's the wan.

Mr. P. You are crazy. If it wasn't too ridiculous I'd boot you off the place for such a suggestion.

P. Now see here, luk at this. [*Pulls paper from his pocket and reads:*] "Wanted, to make the acquaintance of a nice young man. Object—matrimony. Ask for Miss Sarah, at side door of Mr. Parker's house three miles north of Lynn."

Mr. P. Give it here! Let me see it! [*Aside.*] The old fool! Sarah always was silly, but I never would believe this of her; and and at her age. [*Looks blankly at paper for a time.*]

P. Well, are yez satisfied? If so, give me back me paper an' show me the leddy.

Mr. P. (*starting up*). You rascal—(*hesitates, then aside,*) I'll do it! I'll punish her by sending her this fine suitor. [*Aloud.*] Step into the next room. [*Opens door, and ushers* Pat *into the next room.*] Sarah, Sarah, here is some one to see you. [*Closes door and returns to desk.*] Of all things! I only hope none of our friends will see that abominable advertisement. What could have possessed her?

[*Loud voices heard in next room.*] What a disgusted woman she will be. Proposed to by an Irish laborer! Serves her right!

Re-enter PAT.

P. An' a noice wan she is to be advertising for a handsome young man, the ould, gray-headed, wrinkled up ——

MR. P. Be still! Don't you dare to open your head about my sister.

P. Oi've been sold, an' Oi'll hev it out o' yez for this ; trappin' a man into axin' a woman ould enough to be his mother ——

MR. P. Silence! You get out of here, or I'll help you to.

P. Oh, will yez indade. We'll say about that. Oi tell yez I'll hev the law on yez, if yez lift a finger to me ; an' mayhap Oi'll hev it anny way.

MR. P. (*furiously*). Get out, I tell you. [*Goes toward him.* PAT *starts for the door.*]

P. Yes, Oi'll be goin', an' Oi hope as its betther luck yez'll hev wid your adver*tise*ment than Oi've had in answerin' wan.

MR. P. (*rushing at him*). Get out, I say!

PAT *flies through the door, with* MR PARKER *after him.*

[*Curtain falls.*]

THE TRAGEDY OF THE TEN LITTLE BOYS.

A NEW VERSION.

Curtain rises, disclosing ten very little boys sitting on a school bench, and reciting in unison. TEACHER *present.*

⚲EN little schoolboys sitting in a line,
    One fell off, then there were nine.

One falls off the bench and runs away, while the remainder get up and march in line across the stage, reciting :

Nine little schoolboys each with a new slate,
One dropped his and broke it, so there were eight.

One drops his slate, then runs crying off the stage, while the rest stand in a row and recite :

Eight little schoolboys, counting up to eleven,
One got all mixed up, so then there were only seven.
One tries to count, but fails, and retires to the bench as if in disgrace.
Seven little schoolboys playing naughty tricks,
One got caught, and then there were six.
They pinch and pull each other, when the TEACHER *pounces down on them, catches one, puts a dunce cap on him and places him in the corner. The remainder seat themselves, cross-legged, on the floor, and study diligently, a few moments, then recite:*
Six little schoolboys, busy as bees in a hive,
One proved a drone, and so there were five.
They discover that one of their number is falling asleep, instead of studying, so they pounce upon him and carry him out, then come back, form a ring, and recite:
Five little schoolboys, wishing there were more,
One gets his toe stepped on, and then there were four.
One limps out of the circle and off the stage, while the rest jump around and sing:
Four little schoolboys, full of fun and glee;
One thinks it's time to go, and so there are three.
One points to the clock, picks up his hat and books, and runs out. The others recite:
Three little schoolboys! My! what a few!
If another goes away there'll only be two!
They stand and look at one another for a minute, then one tiptoes out. The others play at leap-frog across the stage, and recite:
Two little schoolboys *can* have lots of fun,
Unless one goes away and leaves only one.
One skips out of the door, leaving the other standing disconsolately in middle of stage.
One little schoolboy! Wish I had a gun!
I'd snap it *so* at my head! *Then* there'd be *none!*"
Snaps off an imaginary gun and falls to the ground.
[*Curtain.*]

TABLEAUX.

COMIN' THROUGH THE RYE.

THE tableaux represents the heroine of this popular verse standing to the right of the centre of the stage, with her face turned slightly towards the right, away from the young man, who stands beside her. Her right hand should be raised before her, as if putting him off. Her costume should be a Highland dress of plaid, or a blue skirt and white peasant-waist, with a scarf thrown over her shoulders.

The young man should stand at her left, and just in the act of putting his right arm around her waist, his left hand holding her left to his breast; while his head should be inclined forward, as if attempting to touch her cheek. He should be dressed in striped pants, white shirt, and Scotch cap. A landscape may form the background if scenery is used. Music, "Comin' thro' the Rye."

PUTTING THE CHILDREN TO BED.

TOY bedstead in which are placed two or three dolls. A little girl bending over the bed, with her hand in position for tucking in the bed-clothes.

SUNSHINE OR SHOWER.

THREE little girls with laughing faces are huddled closely together under a large dilapidated umbrella. The umbrella, held open behind them, forms the background of the picture.

DRESSED FOR THE PARTY.

LITTLE girl in party dress, with fan partly open in her hand, is looking backward over her shoulder. Little boy, also in party dress, is holding a bouquet toward the girl.

THE YOUNG ARTIST.

A SMALL boy holding a large slate, on which is partly drawn with chalk a ludicrous outline of a little girl. Standing near the boy is a little girl with the solemn look of importance on her face befitting the occasion of having her portrait made. The boy holds his crayon on the unfinished picture, and he is looking intently at the girl as if studying his subject.

TIRED OUT.

A CHILD asleep in a large chair. One arm thrown over the arm of the chair; the other in his lap, having just loosened his hold of a picture-book, which lies open on his knee. His mouth is a little open, and his head drooped carelessly forward.

A PANTOMIME.

CHRISTMAS EVE.

CHARACTERS AND COSTUMES.—Santa Claus, a large boy, with long, white hair and beard, round fur or paper cap, an enormous pack strapped upon his shoulders, from which protrude various toys. A light carriage-cloth may be wrapped about him. George and Fred—Two little boys, one quite small, dressed in short blouse and pantaloons in Scene I. In Scenes II, III and IV in long colored dressing-gowns. Nellie—Small girl with short dress and apron in Scene I. In Scenes II, III and IV in long white night-robe. Father and Mother—Large boy and girl in ordinary house dress, except the father, as Santa Claus in Scene III.

SCENE I.

THE children come bounding in, they bow to the audience, glance at the clock, go to a small bureau, and opening a drawer, extract three pairs of colored hose. They pin the tops together, and mounting chairs proceed to hang them carefully upon hooks prepared to receive them. Georgie points to the clock, expressing that it is nearly bed-time. Nellie claps her hands, and Fred jumps about and smiles his joy. Taking hold of hands they bow and go out.

SCENE II.

The mother enters with the children, who are robed for sleep. She leads the two youngest, one by each hand. They pause, pointing to the stockings. The mother smiles, and toys with Fred's curls. She leads them to the couch, over which blankets are spread, and kneels in front of the couch, the children follow her example, with clasped hands and bowed heads. They remain in this attitude a short time, then rising, the mother proceeds to assist the two boys into bed, kisses them good-night, looks out of the window, then tucks the covering closer about them. She then leads Nellie to the crib, lifts her in, kisses her, arranges the chairs, closes the drawer that the children left open, takes one more look at the boys and goes out.

Scene III.

Santa Claus comes creeping cautiously in, makes a profound bow to the audience, then peering at the occupants of couch and crib to be sure they are locked in the arms of Morpheus, he proceeds to fill the stockings. While he is thus engaged, the youngest boy (*who should have piercing eyes*) slowly raises his curly head from the pillow, and recognizing his father in the person of Santa Claus, places a finger significantly upon his nose, as much as to say, "You can't fool me." Of course, his movements are unnoticed by Santa Claus, who fills the stockings to repletion, places sundry other large toys, such as a sled, wax doll, hobby, etc., under each respective stocking, and laying a finger upon his lips, bows and goes out.

Scene IV.

The father and mother enter, and going up to the children, pantomine that they are asleep, and must not be disturbed. They sit. Children begin to show signs of waking. Fred leaps to the floor with a bound, rubbing his eyes, the others follow in rapid succession, and mounting chairs, wrench the stockings from the hooks, and scatter their contents over the floor.—(*They should contain nothing that would injure by falling*.)—Fred shakes his finger mischievously at his father, then rushes up and kisses him heartily. The children gather up the toys, which they drop again, and finally, with arms full, they all face the audience, bow and go out.   JENNY JOY.

THE PICKWICKIANS ON ICE.

"NOW," said Wardle, after a substantial lunch, with the agreeable items of strong beer and cherry-brandy, had been done ample justice to, "what say you to an hour on the ice? We shall have plenty of time."

"Capital!" said Mr. Benjamin Allen.

"Prime!" ejaculated Mr. Bob Sawyer.

"You skate, of course, Winkle?" said Wardle.

"Ye—yes; oh, yes!" replied Mr. Winkle. "I—am rather out of practice."

"Oh, do skate, Mr. Winkle," said Arabella. "I like to see it so much!"

"Oh, it is so graceful!" said another young lady.

A third young lady said it was elegant, and a fourth expressed her opinion that it was "swan-like."

"I should be very happy, I'm sure," said Mr. Winkle, reddening; "but I have no skates."

This objection was at once overruled. Trundle had got a couple of pair, and the fat boy announced that there were half a dozen more down stairs; whereat Mr. Winkle expressed exquisite delight, and looked exquisitely uncomfortable.

Old Wardle led the way to a pretty large sheet of ice; and, the fat boy and Mr. Weller having shovelled and swept away the snow which had fallen on it during the night, Mr. Bob Sawyer adjusted his skates with a dexterity which to Mr. Winkle was perfectly marvelious, and described circles with his left leg, and cut figures of eight, and inscribed upon the ice, without once stopping for breath, a great many other pleasant and astonishing devices, to the excessive satisfaction of Mr. Pickwick, Mr. Tupman, and the ladies; which reached a pitch of positive enthusiasm when old Wardle and Benjamin Allen, assisted by the aforesaid Bob Sawyer, performed some mystic evolutions, which they called a reel.

All this time Mr. Winkle, with his face and hands blue with the

11—S. C.

cold, had been forcing a gimlet into the soles of his feet, and putting his skates on with the points behind, and getting the straps into a very complicated and entangled state, with the assistance of Mr. Snod grass, who knew rather less about skates than a Hindoo. At length, owever, with the assistance of Mr. Weller, the unfortunate skates vere firmly screwed and buckled on, and Mr. Winkle was raised to his feet.

" Now, then, sir," said Sam, in an encouraging tone, " off with you, and show 'em how to do it."

"Stop, Sam, stop!" said Mr. Winkle, trembling violently, and clutching hold of Sam's arm with the grasp of a drowning man. "How slippery it is, Sam?"

"Not an uncommon thing upon ice, sir," replied Mr. Weller. "Hold up, sir."

This last observation of Mr. Weller's bore reference to a demonstration Mr. Winkle made, at the instant, of a frantic desire to throw his feet in the air, and dash the back of his head on the ice.

"These—these—are very awkward skates, ain't they, Sam?" inquired Mr Winkle, staggering.

" I'm afeerd there's an orkard gen'lm'n in 'em, sir," replied Sam.

" Now, Winkle," cried Mr. Pickwick, quite unconscious that there was anything the matter. " Come: the ladies are all anxiety."

" Yes, yes," replied Mr. Winkle, with a ghastly smile, " I'm coming."

" Just a-goin' to begin," said Sam, endeavoring to disengage himself. " Now, sir, start off."

"Stop an instant, Sam," gasped Mr. Winkle, clinging most affectionately to Mr. Weller. " I find I've got a couple of coats at home that I don't want Sam. You may have them, Sam."

" Thankee, sir," replied Mr. Weller.

" Never mind touching your hat, Sam," said Mr. Winkle, hastily. "You needn't take your hand away to do that. I meant to have given you five shillings this morning for a Christmas-box, Sam. I'll give it to you this afternoon, Sam."

"You're wery good, sir," replied Mr. Weller.

"Just hold me at first, Sam, will you?" said Mr. Winkle. "There, that's right. I shall soon get in the way of it, Sam. Not too fast, Sam; not too fast!"

Mr. Winkle, stooping forward, with his body half doubled up, was being assisted over the ice by Mr. Weller, in a very singular and unswanlike manner, when Mr. Pickwick most innocently shouted from the opposite bank,—

"Sam!"

"Sir?" said Mr. Weller.

"Here! I want you."

"Let go, sir," said Sam; "don't you hear the governor a-callin'? Let go, sir."

With a violent effort Mr. Weller disengaged himself from the grasp of the agonized Pickwickian; and, in so doing, administered a considerable impetus to the unhappy Mr. Winkle. With an accuracy, which no degree of dexterity or practice could have insured, that unfortunate gentleman bore swiftly down into the centre of the reel, at the very moment when Mr. Bob Sawyer was performing a flourish of unparalleled beauty. Mr. Winkle struck wildly against him, and with a loud crash they fell heavily down. Mr. Pickwick ran to the spot. Bob Sawyer had risen to his feet; but Mr. Winkle was far too wise to do anything of the kind in skates. He was seated on the ice, making spasmodic efforts to smile; but anguish was depicted on every lineament of his countenance.

"Are you hurt?" inquired Mr. Benjamin Allen, with great anxiety.

"Not much," said Mr. Winkle, rubbing his back very hard.

"I wish you would let me bleed you," said Mr. Benjamin Allen, with great eagerness.

"No; thank you," replied Mr. Winkle, hurriedly.

"I really think you had better," said Mr. Allen.

"Thank you," replied Mr. Winkle; "I'd rather not."

"What do you think, Mr. Pickwick?" inquired Bob Sawyer.

Mr. Pickwick was excited and indignant. He beckoned to Mr Weller, and said, in a stern voice, " Take his skates off."

" No ; but really I had scarcely begun," remonstrated Mr. Winkle.

"Take his skates off," repeated Mr. Pickwick, firmly.

The command was not to be resisted.   Mr. Winkle allowed Sam to obey it in silence.

"Lift him up," said Mr. Pickwick.   Sam assisted him to rise.

Mr. Pickwick retired a few paces apart from the by-standers ; and, beckoning his friend to approach, fixed a searching look upon him, and uttered in a low but distinct and emphatic tone, these remarkable words :

" You're a humbug, sir."

" A what ? " said Mr. Winkle, starting

" A humbug, sir. I will speak plainer, if you wish it. An im-poster, sir."

With these words Mr. Pickwick turned slowly on his heel, and rejoined his friends.

While Mr. Pickwick was delivering himself of the sentiment just recorded, Mr. Weller and the fat boy, having by their joint endeavors cut out a slide, were exercising themselves thereupon in a very masterly and brilliant manner. Sam Weller, in particular, was display-ing that beautiful feat of fancy sliding, which is currently denominated " knocking at the cobbler's door," and which is achieved by skimming over the ice on one foot, and occasionally giving a two-penny post-man's knock upon it with the other. It was a good long slide ; and there was something in the motion, which Mr. Pickwick, who was very cold with standing still, could not help envying.

" It looks a nice, warm exercise, that, doesn't it ? " he inquired of Wardle, when that gentleman was thoroughly out of breath, by reason of the indefatigable manner, in which he had converted his legs into a pair of compasses, and drawn complicated problems on the ice.

" Ah, it does, indeed," replied Wardle.   " Do you slide ? "

" I used to do so on the gutters, when I was a boy," replied Mr. Pickwick.

"Try it now," said Wardle.

"Oh, do please, Mr. Pickwick!" cried all the ladies.

"I should be very happy to afford you any amusement," replied Mr. Pickwick; "but I haven't done such a thing these thirty years."

"Pooh: pooh: nonsense!" said Wardle, dragging off his skates with the impetuosity which characterized all his proceedings. "Here! I'll keep you company; come along." And away went the good-tempered old fellow down the slide with a rapidity, which came very close upon Mr. Weller, and beat the fat boy all to nothing.

Mr. Pickwick paused, considered, pulled off his gloves and put them in his hat, took two or three short runs, balked himself as often, and at last took another run, and went slowly and gravely down the slide, with his feet about a yard and a quarter apart, amidst the gratified shouts of all the spectators.

"Keep the pot a-bilin', sir," said Sam; and down went Wardle again, and then Mr. Pickwick, and then Sam, and then Mr. Winkle, and then Mr. Bob Sawyer, and then the fat boy, and then Mr. Snodgrass; following closely upon each other's heels, and running after each other with as much eagerness as if all their future prospects in life depended on their expedition.

It was the most intensely interesting thing to observe the manner, in which Mr. Pickwick performed his share in the ceremony; to watch the torture of anxiety with which he viewed the person behind gaining upon him at the imminent hazard of tripping him up: to see him gradually expend the painful force which he had put on at first, and turn slowly round on the slide, with his face towards the point from which he started; to contemplate the playful smile which mantled on his face when he had accomplished the distance, and the eagerness with which he turned round when he had done so, and ran after his predecessor, his black gaiters tripping pleasantly through the snow, and his eyes beaming cheerfulness and gladness through his spectacles. And when he was knocked down (which happened upon the average every third round), it was the most invigorating sight that could possibly be imagined, to behold him gather up his hat, gloves and handkerchief with a glowing countenance, and resume his station in the rank with an ardor and enthusiasm which nothing could abate.

The sport was at its height, the sliding was at the quickest, the laughter was at the loudest, when a sharp, smart crack was heard. There was a quick rush towards the bank, a wild scream from the ladies and a shout from Mr. Tupman. A large mass of ice disappeared, the water bubbled up over it, and Mr. Pickwick's hat, gloves and handkerchief were floating on the surface; and this was all of Mr. Pickwick that anybody could see.

Dismay and anguish were depicted on every countenance; the males turned pale, and the females fainted; Mr. Snodgrass and Mr. Winkle grasped each other by the hand, and gazed at the spot, where their leader had gone down, with frenzied eagerness; while Mr. Tupman, by way of rendering the promptest assistance, and at the same time conveying to any person who might be within hearing the clearest possible notion of the catastrophe, ran off across the country at his utmost speed, screaming "Fire!" with all his might and main.

It was at this very moment, when old Wardle and Sam Weller were approaching the hole with cautious steps, and Mr. Benjamin Allen was holding a hurried consultation with Mr. Bob Sawyer on the advisibility of bleeding the company generally, as an improving little bit of professional practice,—it was at this very moment that a face, head and shoulders emerged from beneath the water, and disclosed the features and spectacles of Mr. Pickwick.

" Keep yourself up for an instant, for only one instant," bawled Mr. Snodgrass.

" Yes—do : let me implore you—for my sake," roared Mr. Winkle, deeply affected. The adjuration was rather unnecessary ; the probability being, that, if Mr. Pickwick had not decided to keep himself up for anybody else's sake, it would have occurred to him that he might as well do so for his own.

" Do you feel the bottom there, old fellow?" said Wardle.

"Yes—certainly," replied Mr. Pickwick, wringing the water from his head and face, and gasping for breath. "I fell upon my back. I couldn't get on my feet at first."

The clay upon so much of Mr. Pickwick's coat as was yet visible bore testimony to the accuracy of this statement; and, as the fears of the spectators were still further relieved by the fat boy's suddenly recollecting that the water was nowhere more than five feet deep, prodigies of valor were performed to get him out. After a vast quantity of splashing and cracking and struggling, Mr. Pickwick was at length fairly extricated from his unpleasant situation, and once more stood on dry land.

Mr. Pickwick was wrapped up, and started off for home, presenting a singular phenomenon of an elderly gentleman dripping wet, and without a hat, with his arms bound down to his sides, skimming over the ground without any clearly-defined purpose, at the rate of six good English miles an hour.—CHARLES DICKENS.

A TUXEDO ROMANCE.

'TWAS at Tuxedo—let me see—
 In late September, long ago;
 Yes, eighteen hundred eighty-three.
But how time flies; and yet I know
It's nine years since I passed my nights
 Here at Tuxedo—filled my glass
Of life with pleasures and delights,
 And let some golden chances pass.

For they *were* golden, if we count
 An opportunity to wed
A stunning girl, and wedding mount
 The social scale. Who was it said—
And said it wisely, if he knew it?—
 "Ambition is a dangerous tool,
When used too freely we may rue it,
 By sovereign, or sage or fool."

In those days Gertrude was a queen,
  A social queen, and winsome, too.
Her hair was brown, with just a sheen
  Of gold and amber shining through,
And how we flirted!   We had met
  At Newport in the busy whirl
Which July brings.   I liked her set;
  'Twas ultra—and I liked the girl.

I more than liked her.   Now it seems
  'Twas love's first dawning; I was young,
And there was time for golden dreams.
  We drove, we chatted, danced and sung
Together, for the season's close
  Was well upon us.   Butterflies
And moths alike, the whole world knows,
  Will seek the bright and fairest skies

Society had turned its back
  On rare Tuxedo; but we stayed,
And certainly there seemed no lack
  Of pleasure, for she had delayed
Her trip to London, where with rage
  Her father waited.   Then, one day—
To fill life's darkest, saddest page—
  She sobbed, and sobbing went away.

We corresponded every week,
  Such letters that I wonder now
The steamer did not spring a leak,
  Scorched and consumed from stern to prow.
They burned with passion and with love;
  They vowed that while our lives should last
We'd be as true as stars above,
  And all such nonsense.   Now 'tis past.

Her letters stopped; I sought the whirl
  Of social pleasures; then for spite
I wooed and wed another girl.
  I did not half deserve the bright
And happy life she brought me. So
  'Twas not until to-night I found
Myself once more within the flow
  Of Fashion's set and Fashion's sound.

I waltzed once with my partner's wife,
  Then in an alcove by the door—
My veins seemed filled with fresh, new life—
  I saw a face I'd known before—
'Twas Gertrude. Springing to her side
  I poured forth words of passion, then
This girl, who should have been my bride,
  Said: "Jack, you're just like other men,

And I like other women, too.
  Once we were foolish, long ago,
But, really, I supposed you knew
  'Twas only a flirtation; so
You see I made the best of fate,
  And married quite another one.
Dear Jack, I fear you've come too late—
  But let me introduce my son."   ALBERT HARDY.

BOOH !

[Read at the Literary Congress in Chicago, Children's Day.]

ON afternoons, when baby boy has had a splendid nap
  And sits, like any monarch on his throne in nurse's lap,
In this peculiar wise I hold my 'kerchief to my face,
And cautiously and quietly I move about the place;
Then, with a cry, I suddenly expose my face to view,
And you should hear him laugh and crow when I say "Booh!"

Sometimes that rascal tries to make believe that he is scared,
And, really, when I first began, he stared and stared and stared;
And then his under lip came out and further out it came,
Till mamma and the nurse agreed it was a "cruel shame."
But now what does the same wee, toddling, lisping baby do
But laugh and kick his little heels when I say "Booh!"

He laughs and kicks his little heels in rapturous glee, and then
In shrill, despotic treble bids me "do it all aden!"
And I—of course I do it for, as his progenitor,
It is such pretty, pleasant play as this that I am for!
And it is, oh, such fun! and I am sure that I shall rue
The time when we are both too old to play the game of "Booh!"

EUGENE FIELD.

AWFULLY LOVELY PHILOSOPHY.

A FEW days ago a Boston girl who had been at the School of Philosophy at Concord, arrived in Brooklyn, on a visit to a seminary chum. After canvassing thoroughly the fun and gum-drops that made up their education in the seat of learning at which their early scholastic efforts were made, the Brooklyn girl began to inquire the nature of the Concord entertainment.

"And so you are taking lessons in philosophy! How do you like it?"

"Oh, it's perfectly lovely! It's about science, you know, and we all just dote on science."

"It must be nice. What is it about?"

"It's about molecules as much as anything else, and molecules are all just too awfully nice for anything. If there's anything I really enjoy it's molecules."

"Tell me about them, my dear. What are molecules?"

"Oh, molecules! They are little wee things, and it takes ever so many of them. They are splendid things. Do you know there ain't anything but what's got molecules in it. And Mr. Cook is just as sweet as he can be, and Mr. Emerson, too. They explain everything so beautifully."

"How I'd like to go there!" said the Brooklyn girl, enviously.

"You'd enjoy it ever so much. They teach protoplasm, too, and if there is one thing perfectly heavenly, it's protoplasm. I really don't know which I like best, protoplasm or molecules."

"Tell me about protoplasm. I know I should adore it."

"'Deed, you would. It's just too sweet to live. You know it's about how things get started, or something of that kind. You ought to hear Mr. Emerson tell about it. It would stir your very soul. The first time he explained about protoplasm there wasn't a dry eye in the house. We named our hats after him. This is an Emerson hat. You see the ribbon is drawn over the crown and caught with a buckle and a bunch of flowers. Then you turn up the side with a spray of forget-me-nots. Ain't it just too sweet? All the girls in the school have them."

"How exquisitely lovely! Tell me some more science."

"Oh, I almost forgot about differentiation. I am really and truly positively in love with differentiation. It's different from molecules and protoplasm, but it's every bit as nice. And Mr. Cook! You should hear him go on about it. I really believe he's perfectly bound up in it. This scarf is the Cook scarf. All the girls wear them, and we named them after him, just on account of the interest he takes in differentiation."

"What is it, anyway?"

"This is mull, trimmed with Languedoc lace——"

"I don't mean that—that other."

"Oh, differentiation! Ain't it sweet? It's got something **to do** with species. It's the way you tell one hat from another, so you'll know which is becoming. And we learn all about ascidians, too. They are the divinest things! I'm absolutely enraptured with ascidians. If I only had an ascidian of my own! I wouldn't ask anything else in the world."

"What do they look like, dear? Did you ever see one?" asked the Brooklyn girl, deeply interested.

"Oh, no: nobody ever saw one except Mr. Cook and Mr. Emerson; but they are something like an oyster with a reticule hung on its belt. I think they are just heavenly."

"Do you learn anything else besides?"

"Oh, yes. We learn about common philosophy and logic, and those common things like metaphysics; but the girls don't care anything about those. We are just in ecstacies over differentiations and molecules, and Mr. Cook and protoplasms, and ascidians and Mr. Emerson, and I really don't see why they put in those vulgar branches. If anybody, beside Mr. Cook and Mr. Emerson, had done it, we should have told him to his face that he was too terribly, awfully mean."

And the Brooklyn girl went to bed that night in the dumps, because fortune had not vouchsafed her the advantages enjoyed by her friend.

"WASH DOLLY UP LIKE THAT."

[Child dialect.]

"I'LL be the goodest little girl
That ever you did see,
If you'll let me take my dolly
To church with you and me,
It's too drefful bad to leave her
When we's all gone away;
Oh! Cosette will be so lonesome
To stay at home all day."

'Twas such a pleading pair of eyes
And winsome little face
That mamma couldn't well refuse,
Though church was not the place
For dolls or playthings she well knew,
Still mamma's little maid

Was always so obedient
  She didn't feel afraid.

No mouse was ever half so still
  As this sweet little lass,
Until the sermon was quite through—
  Then this did come to pass:
A dozen babies (more or less)
  Dressed in long robes of white
Were brought before the altar rail—
  A flash of heaven's own light.

Then Mabel stood upon the seat,
  With dolly held out straight,
And this is what the darling said:
  "Oh! minister, please to wait,
And wash my dolly up like that—
  Her name it is Cosette.
The "minister" smiled and bowed his head,
  But mamma blushes yet.

PROOF POSITIVE.

I STEPPED into my room one day
  And saw some children there at play.
  I sought my little girl and found her
  With half a dozen youngsters round her;
  And from the way she slapped her rule,
  I knew that they were "playing school."

I gave my little girl a kiss—
A pleasure that I never miss.

A murmur through the school-room ran,
  A smile pervaded every feature,
"He must be a committeeman!"
  They loud exclaimed—"he kissed the teacher!"

THE SONG OF THE PRINTING PRESS.

[Written expressly for this Volume.]

I'M a king among men, and no monarch of old,
　Whose valorous deeds to the world have been told,
　Ever ruled in a kingdom so wide as my own,
　Or graced with his purple so mighty a throne.

From the warm brain of genius I sprang at a bound,
With bolts, screws and pinions, and cylinders round,
Ink-fountains and cranks, mighty levers and rings,
Wide feed-boards and buffer-wheels, gear-wheels and springs

I have pulleys and rollers, belts, grippers and flies—
No finer machinery man's brain could devise;
They made me with hammer, file, chisel and fire—
Though I go night and day, yet my wheels never tire.

In each crank, in each spring, in each wheel is a thought,
And into cold iron man's mind has been wrought;
There is life in the crank, in the spring, in the wheel;
There is brain in the levers and blood in the steel.

Though silent and dead to all eyes I may seem,
I start into life at the hiss of the steam;
My axles are oiled and my cylinders fleet,
My dizzy wheels whirl and my wild pulses beat.

Like the snowflakes descending in clouds from the sky,
The fresh-printed sheets from my deft fingers fly;
They rustle, they flutter, they drop thick and fast
As leaves from the trees in the hurricane's blast.

I print what I get—telegraphic despatches,
Births, weddings, elopments, divorces and matches;
Things wondrous and witty, things foolish and wise—
It is said that I've even been known to print lies.

I know all the news and I tell it to you—
Frauds, forgeries, murders, and politics, too;
Ball matches and accidents, weather reports,
And naughty flirtations at summer resorts.

Mrs. Snooks made a call, and the rich Mrs. Scroggs
Gave a party and didn't invite Mrs. Noggs;
Two dogs had a fight, and the Smiths had a row—
I have printed it all, and the world knows it now.

I print the price-lists of the market in stocks,
Long columns of gossip and very stale jokes;
Queer stories of tadpoles and spiders and leeches,
Quack remedies, lost curs, and Congressmen's speeches.

One man is just crazy to try matrimony,
Provided the widow has plenty of money;
Another's so lonely he must advertise,
For a lovely brunette with bewitching black eyes.

I tell what is wanted, and where you may look
For a trim dancing master, a nursemaid or cook,
A repairer of bric-a-brac, shoes and old clothes,
Or a genteel professor of corns and sore toes.

But these common achievements 'tis time to dismiss,
For my type has a purpose far higher than this;
I create the opinion that rules ev'ry nation,
And grandly lead onward all civilization.

Old Vulcan, the blacksmith, grim, sooty and dire,
Forged hot thunderbolts with his anvil and fire,
And the bolts from Olympus like lightning were hurled
By Jupiter Tonans, the king of the world.

When my forces were forged into being and birth,
I received for my kingdom the realms of the earth.

And was clothed with a sway that was destined to **prove**
Far grander than that of Olympian Jove.

I send forth the Bible, the classic, the story ;
I tell of brave deeds and the patriot's glory,
I issue great thoughts and they fly like the light,
That shoots its sharp gleams through the gloom of **the night.**

To the millions who read I'm commissioned to state
What histories tell and what fictions narrate,
What science proclaims, what theology preaches,
What invention finds out, what philosophy teaches.

Now my noise is the song which some great poet sings,
Now the burning oration that thunders and rings,
Now the sweet tale of love, now the advocate's plea,
Now the message that flashes from under the sea.

Make the furnaces hot, and the steam—crowd it on
Till my mission is ended, my laurels are won,
And the world, all renewed, shall applaud and confess
It was fashioned anew by the swift printing press.

HENRY DAVENPORT.

POMONA DESCRIBES HER BRIDAL TRIP.

"NOW, then, says Jone, after he'd been thinkin' a while, ' there'll be no more foolin' on this trip. To-morrow we'll go to father's, an' if the old gentleman has got any money on the crops, which I expect he has by this time, I'll take up a part of my share, an' we'll have a trip to Washington an' see the President, an' Congress, an' the White House, an' the lamp always a-burnin' before the Supreme Court, an'—'

"' Don't say no more,' says I ; ' it's splendid !'

" So early the nex' day we goes off jus' as fast as trains would take us to his father's, an' we hadn't been there more'n ten minutes before Jone found out he had been summoned on a jury.

JOSEPH JEFFERSON and BLANCHE BENDER

in "Rip Van Winkle."

(Suggestion for Tableau)

INDIAN COSTUME—Suggestion for a Tableau

" ' When must you go ? ' says I, when he come, lookin' kind o' pale, to tell me this.

" ' Right off,' says he. 'The court meets this mornin'. If I don't hurry up I'll have some of 'em after me. But I wouldn't cry about it. I don't believe the case'll last more'n a day.'

" The old man harnessed up an' took Jone to the court house, an' I went too, for I might as well keep up the idea of a bridal trip as not. I went up into the gallery an' Jone he was set among the other men in the jury-box.

" The case was about a man named Brown, who married the half sister of a man named Adams, who afterward married Brown's mother an' sold Brown a house he had got from Brown's grandfather in trade for half a grist mill, which the other half of it was owned by Adams's half sister's first husband, who left all his property to a Soup Society, in trust, till his son should come of age, which he never did, but left a will which gave his half of the mill to Brown; an' the suit was between Brown an' Adams an' Brown again, an' Adams's half-sister, who was divorced from Brown, an' a man named Ramsey, who had put up a new over-shot wheel to the grist mill.

" That case wasn't a easy one to understand, as you may see for yourselves, an' it didn't get finished that day. They argyed over it a full week. When there wasn't no more witnesses to carve up, one lawyer made a speech, an' he set that crooked case so straight that you could see through it from the over-shot wheel clean back to Brown's grandfather. Then another feller made a speech an' he set the whole thing up another way. It was jus' as clear to look through but it was another case altogether, no more like the other one than a apple pie is like a mug o' cider. An' then they both took it up, an' they swung it around between 'em till it was all twisted an' knotted an' wound up an' tangled worse than a skein o' yarn in a nest o' kittens, an' then they give it to the jury.

" Well, when them jurymen went out there wasn't none of 'em, as Jone told me afterward, as knew whether it was Brown or Adams as was dead, or whether the mill was to grind soup or to be run by soup

12—S. C.

power. Of course, they couldn't agree. Three of 'em wanted to
give a verdict for the boy that died, two of 'em was for Brown's
grandfather, an' the rest was scattered, some goin' in for damages to
the witnesses, who ought to get somethin' for havin' their characters
ruined. Jone he jus' held back ready to jine the other eleven as soon
as they'd agree. But they couldn't do it, an' they was locked up
three days an' four nights. You'd better believe I got pretty wild
about it, but I come to court every day an' waited, bringin' somethin'
.o eat in a basket. Jone never had no chance to jine in with the other
fellers, for they couldn't agree, an' they were all discharged at last.
So the whole thing went for nothin'. When Jone come out he looked
like he'd been drawn through a pump-log, and he says to me, tired
like :

   " ' Let's go home an' settle down ! ' "—FRANK R. STOCKTON.

CAUSE AND EFFECT.

A LITTLE dinner party was in progress down below,
        While above stairs, in the nursery, was a lovely little Fred.
    "There is nothing left to do !" he sighed, "that clock is very
        slow,
        And when nurse does finish supper she will put me straight
        to bed!

" Now, if they'd let me play with that ! "—he looked up on the wall,
    And gently pushed a chair along before him as he spoke,
" I really would not mischief it, or worry it at all,
    And I feel quite pretty certain I could mend it if it broke !"

About five minutes after this the door bell rang, and low
    The servant to the master whispered, " Sir, he's at the door—
The messenger you rang for."   Replied the master, " No ;
    He's made some stupid blunder," and he thought of it no more.

Five minutes passed ; a sound of wheels ; the servant came to say,
    "The carriage is awaiting, sir—belike its come too early,

"But the man is very positive you rang for a cuppay."
  "I didn't!" said the master, and his look and tone were surly.

In the same mysterious manner a policeman came and went,
  And a doubtful look was growing now upon the master's face,
An idea had occurred to him of what the mystery meant,
  And he was just preparing to follow out the trace—

When lo! a burst of thunder sound—the engine drew up proudly,
  Close followed by the hose cart, and dire confusion grew,
But the master from his doorstep by shouting wildly, loudly,
  Was in time to stop the deluge, and 'twas all that he could do.

Straightway to the alarm he went and captured Master Freddy,
  Who sobbed "I only give it such a little, little jerk!
I didn't mean to start it—just to try if it was ready;
  I wanted—all I wanted was to see if it would work"

THE PUZZLED DUTCHMAN.

I'M a broken-hearted Deutscher,
    Vot's villed mit crief und shame,
  I dells you vot der drouple ish:
    I doesn't know my name.

You dinks dis fery vunny, eh?
    Ven you der schtory hear,
  You vill not vonder den so mooch,
    It vas so schtrange and queer.

Mine moder had dwo leedle twins;
    Dey vas me und mine broder:
  Ve lookt so fery mooch alike,
    No von knew vich vrom toder.

Von off der poys was "Yawcob,"
   Und "Hans" der oder's name:
But den it made no tifferent :
   Ve both got called der same.

Vell! von off us got tead—
   Yaw, Mynheer, dot ish so!
But vedder Hans or Yawcob,
   Mine moder she don't know.

Und so I am in drouples :
   I gan't kit droo mine hed
Vedder I'm Hans vot's lifing,
   Or Yawcob vot is tead!

                       CHARLES F. ADAMS

MRS. SMART LEARNS HOW TO SKATE.

DON'T you think skating is dreadful good exercise? I do, and I've been trying of it lately, so that I have as good a knowledge of how it operates as anybody else.

Joshua said I was rather old to go into such childish bizness : but I don't see no airthly reason why an old married woman shouldn't enjoy herself if she can. Goodness knows, most of us has trouble enough to put up with—if we have a husband and children and hens and pigs and things. And if we can git any enjoyment out of life, I say we'd orter. I calkulate to, myself; and I'd like to see anybody hender me! It'll take more'n Joshua Smart! He never growed big enuff! No, sir! not by a long chalk!

All the folks round about here has gone into skating. There hain't nobody but what's had a spell at it. Even old Grandmarm Smith, that's gone with two canes this dozen years—she's tried it, and fell down, and smashed her specs, and barked her nose all to flinchers; and old Deacon Sharp, that's been blind ever since Wiggin's barn was burnt, he's got to be quite a powerful skater. Only you have to clear the track when you see him coming, 'cause he don't turn out for nobody nor nothing. And he's apt to git to using big words, if he happens to hit against anything. The other day he skated against a tall stump in the millpond, and a madder man you never seed. He took it for somebody standing there; and, if he is a deacon, I'm ready to give my Bible oath that he came at it, and hit it several licks with his fist, afore he found out that it wasn't no one.

All the wimmen folks has been out on the ice this fall. I never seed such a turnout afore. The way they've done, they've cooked up enuff Satterdays to last all through the next week, and then they've skated, and their husbands has staid at home, and swore and eat cold vittles.

Law sake! how things have changed since I was a gal! The world is gitting more and more civilized every day. In a thousand years from now, at the present rate of getting along, this airth will be too good to live in, and most of us will have to leave, if we hain't already.

Why, I can remember when a gal that dared to look at a pair of skates was called a Tomboy; and you might as well have served out a term in the States Prison as to have been called that! It was an awful name! It used to be a sin for a gal to do anything that a boy did, except milk the cows, and eat pudding and molasses.

As soon as it got cold enough to friz up, I made up my mind to see what I could do at skating. I had an idea that it wouldn't take me no time at all to larn. All the gals was an awful spell a-larning; but all in the world that made 'em so long was 'cause they had fellers a-showing of 'em how, and they kinder liked the fun. If there hadn't been a feller in the neighborhood, a'most any of 'em would larnt the whole trade in three days.

I went over to the bridge, and sold five pounds of butter, and got me a pair of skates. Hain't it astonishing how butter has gone up? Never seed the beat of it in all my life! We don't pretend to eat a mite of butter to our house, though we've got three farrer cows and a new milk's heifer. Joshua grumbles like everything; but I tell him 'taint no use—I'd as lives he'd spread his bread with fifty-cent scrips as with butter. And 'twon't make no difference a hundred years from now whetner a man has lived on butter or hog's fat. Not a speck!

I sold the butter, and took three dollars' worth of skates. Miss Pike, the milliner, said I ought to have a skating costume—it wasn't properous to skate in a long-tailed gownd and crinoline.

So one day I sot myself to work, and fixed one. I took a pair of Joshua's red flannel drawers, and sot two rosettes of green ribbon onto the bottoms of 'em; and then I took a yaller petticoat of mine, and sewed five rows of blue braids round the bottom of that; my waist I made out of a red and brown plaid shawl, and for a cap I took one of Joshua's cast-off stove-pipe hats, and cut it down a story. I tied a wide piece of red flannel around it, and pulled out an old crower's tail, and stuck that into the front of it. Joshua laffed at me, the master. He sed I looked jest like an Injun squaw; but as he never seed one, I dunno how he knowed.

Sam Jellison sed he'd larn me how to do; but I told him no; I didn't want nobody a-handling me round a-finding out whether I wore corsets or not. I didn't like the style. I guessed I could take keer of myself. I'd allers managed to. I'd took keer of myself through the jonders, and the dispepsy, and the collery morbus, and I'd allers made my soap, and did my own cleaning, and I guessed I could skate without nobody's assistance. I didn't want no little upstarts a holding onto me with one arm, and laffing at me in t'other sleeve at the same time.

Sam he whistled and sed nothing. It's a dreadful hateful way some folks have of insulting of ye—that whistle of theirn.

One Tuesday morning, bright and airly, I got my work out of the way, and dressing myself in my skating costume, I took my skates in one hand and a long pole to steady myself by in the other, and set sail for the mill-pond.

I shouldn't have dared to begin such an undertaking any day but Tuesday. Wednesday is allers a dreadful day for me! Why, I've broke more'n ten dollars' worth of crockery Wednesdays; and I've sot three hens Wednesdays, and one's eggs all addled, and one she got broke up afore sh'd sot a week, and t'other one hatched out three chickens that was blind as bats, and never had no tail-feathers!

I went so airly, that I was in hopes there wouldn't be no speckle-petaters to see my fust attempt; but, lawful heart! the pond was lined with 'em! I felt rather down in the mouth at the idea of trying my skill afore all them people, but I was too plucky to back out.

I sot down on the ground, and strapped on my skates; and grabbing my pole firmly in both hands, I got onto the ice. The minnit I got on, I sot rite down flat, in spite of all I could do, and it was as much as five minutes afore I could git up agin. And when I did my left foot begun for to run rite round t'other one, and I run rite round arter it. The fust thing I knowed my heels was up, and my head was down, and I thought it was night and all the stars in the firmary was having a shooting-match.

Sam Jellison he seed me fall, and come and picked me up. Sam is dreadful attentive to me, because he's trying to shine my darter Betsey. I can see through it all. He wanted to help me stiddy myself, but I wouldn't let him, and started off upon the dog trot. I could run a good deal better than I could slide. I thought I'd go over on t'other side of the pond, where Miss Pike and some other friends of mine was; and, sticking my long pole into the airholes, I made out to get under way. And after I once got started, the difficulty was to stop myself. I went rite ahead like a steam injine down grade. I found it wasn't no use to fite against fate; and, concluding that this was the fun of skating, I drawed up my pole and let it stick out each side of me, and sailed on. I had the wind in my back, and it filled my yaller petticoat so that it floated out afore me like the star spangled banner on the Fourth of July.

I was a-coming to where the skaters were at it pretty thick; but I I didn't think to take my pole in, and the fust thing I knowed I was a mowing of 'em down with it, rite and left, as a two-hoss mowing-machine takes down the grass on a medder.

The ice was lined with the ruins! Muffs, and hoods, and gloves, and false teeth, and waterfalls, and rats, and mice, and curled hair, and men, and women, and little boys—all mixed up together. You couldn't tell t'other from which!

Old Jim Pratt he went down among the rest; and, as he went, the toe of his skate ketched into that beautiful braid on my yaller petticoat, and in less'n a minnit tore it clear off and wound it all among the understandings of all the scrabbling people.

I was madder'n a hatter! I riz my pole to let 'em have some; but before I could strike, the strain on that illigant trimming upsot my equalibrius, and down I went, striking the back of my crannyrum so hard, that for a minnit I thought my skull bone was broke clean across! It seemed as if I could hear the rough edges grate together.

Just as I was a-rising to get up, along come a feller at a 2.40 rate, without any eyes into his head, I expect, for he didn't see me, but undertook to skate rite over me, and away he come, head fust, onto the ice, with a grunt that sounded like a pig's when he's just gwine to sleep after eating a whole pail of swill.

I grabbed hold of his coat-tail to hist myself up by, and, law sake! the cloth parted like a cobweb, and left him with a short jacket on, and letting me back onto the ice harder than afore!

Sam Jellison he arrived jest at this minnit, and I didn't say nothing agin his helping of me. I felt as if I was nigh about played out. He esquarted me to the shore, with all that blue braid a-trailing after me. And when I'd got breath, he went up home with me, and I heard him kiss Bets behind the pantry door. Wall, wall, young folks will be young folks, and 'tain't no use to try to hinder 'em.

I was so sore for a week that I couldn't git my arms to my head without screeching, and I felt all over as if I'd been onjinted and jined onto another person's understandings.

As soon as I got better, though, I let Sam help me larn, and I can skate the master now. You never seed the beat! Its the grandest exercise! and so healthy! I've friz both of my feet, and my nose and my face has mostly peeled, and I've got the rumatiz tremenjous; but I've larned to skate. and what do I keer!—CLARA AUGUSTA.

A BOY'S POEM ON WASHINGTON.

[Written expressly for this volume.]

THEY'RE making a fuss about George's birthday—
  Who cares for his birthday?   Not I;
'Tisn't much of a day for us boys after all—
  I'd rather have Fourth of July.

Of course, ev'rybody has got to be born,
  And a birthday will come now and then,
I know folks who have it about every year,
  But that doesn't make them great men.

George hacked at a cherry tree, so it is said,
  And then wouldn't make an excuse;
Why should he? His father had seen what he did,
  To lie would have been of no use.

Our country once wanted a father, you know;
  If George hadn't then been around
Some other would soon have applied for the place,
  And a good situation have found.

Besides, it's a shame to make George the father
  Of a country so great and so grand,
When nothing whatever is said of a mother—
  Why, that's a mean slight to our land.

Uncle Ben's got a picture of George in a boat,
  A-crossing the Delaware River.
Well, how would he cross it except in a boat?
  Wade through it, get wet and then shiver?

My history says that a winter he spent
  At a place that is called Valley Forge;

What of it? Why people spend winters there now—
    Was that any credit to George?

He got the gilt sword of Cornwallis, 'tis said,
    And that was the end of the bother;
And yet, all the time he'd a sword of his own,
    And why should he want any other?

A president then I believe he was made,
    But that wasn't much it would seem;
'Twould have been something like it if he'd only been
    At the head of a foot-ball team.

                         HENRY DAVENPORT.

HOW THREE WERE MADE ONE.

[The figures refer to the corresponding numbers in Part I.]

A CANNIBAL maid and her Hottentot Blade—
    They met[2] in a rocky defile;
A gay eagle plume[16] was his only costume,
    The lady was wrapt in a—smile;
Together they strolled, and his passion[3] he told
    In pleading[18] and tremulous tone,
While softly they trod on the blossom-strewn sod,
    And spooned in the twilight alone.

Then sweetly she sighed as she shyly replied,
    With tender and fairy-like mien;
She murmured the word, when a war whoop[22] was heard
    A rival had burst[2] on the scene.
A savage Zulu to the trysting place drew,
    Demanding[4] his Cannibal bride;
But the Hottentot said, with a toss of his head,
    "I'll have thy[2] degenerate hide!"

The Hottentot flew at the savage Zulu,
 The Zulu he went for the Blade,
And fiercely they vied[14] in their strength and their pride,
 And fought[2] for the Cannibal Maid.
She perched on a stone,[9] with a shapely shinbone
 Clasped tight in her tapering arms,
And watched the blood fly with a love-laden eye
 While the warriors fought for her charms.

When fiercer they fought and the ringing blows caught
 With thrust and with parry and punch,
She said, with a smile, " In a very short while
 I will have those[9] two fellows for lunch."
The purple blood flows from the Hottentot's nose,
 The Zulu is struck by the Blade;
Then each of them sighed,[19] a gasping—he died,
 And looked on the Cannibal Maid.

She made a nice stew of the savage Zulu,
 And scrambled the Hottentot's brains—
Twas a dainty menu when the cooking was through,
 And she dined on her lovers' remains.
The savage Zulu and the Hottentot, too,
 Both sleep in a Cannibal[7] tomb;
The three were made one, and the story is done—
 The maiden strolled[9] off in the gloom.

EDWARD H. PEALE.

THE GOAT AND THE SWING.

A VICIOUS goat, one day, had found
 His way into forbidden ground,
 When, coming to the garden swing,
He spied a most prodigious thing—
A ram, a monster to his mind,
With head before and head behind!

Its shape was odd, no hoofs were seen,
But without legs it stood between
Two upright, lofty posts of oak,
With forehead ready for a stroke.

Though but a harmless ornament
Carved on the seat, it seemed intent
On barring the intruder's way;
While he, advancing, seemed to say,
"Who is this surly fellow here?
Two heads, no tail—it's mighty queer!
A most insulting countenance!"
With stamp of foot and angry glance
He curbed his threatening neck, and stood
Before the passive thing of wood.

"You winked as I was going by!
You didn't? What! tell me I lie?
Take that!" and at the swing he sprung;
A sounding thump! It backward swung,
And, set in motion by the blow,
Swayed menacingly to and fro.

"Ha! you'll fight? A quarrelsome chap
I knew you were! You'll get a rap!
I'll crack your skull!" A headlong jump;
Another and a louder bump!

The swing, as if with kindling wrath,
Came pushing back along the path.
The goat, astonished, shook his head,
Winked hard, turned round, grew mad and said,
"Villain! I'll teach you who I am!"
(Or seemed to say), "you rascal ram,
To pick a fight with me, when I

So quietly am passing by!
Your head or mine!"   A thundering stroke:
The cracking horns met crashing oak!

Then came a dull and muffled sound,
And something rolled along the ground,
Got up, looked sad, appeared to say:
"Your head's too hard!" and limped away
Quite humbly, in a rumpled coat—
A dirtier and a wiser goat!

JOHN TOWNSEND TROWBRIDGE.

THE McSWATS SWEAR OFF.

[Without speaking the word "puff" imitate the puff of one smoking.]

"LOBELIA, my love, another long and delightful evening is before us."

The young husband was arrayed in a dressing-gown of gorgeous, variegated and dazzling complexion.   He sat in a luxurious armchair and rested his tired feet on the soft plush cushions of two other chairs.   In his hand he held a magazine of large print which he was trying laboriously to read with the aid of an eye-glass he had purchased under the deep and solemn conviction that his position in society required him to use something of the kind.

"Is there anything else I can do for your comfort, Billiger?" tenderly inquired the young wife.

"I think not, Lobelia," he replied after considering a few moments; "though if you will kindly open that package of 'Lone Jack' and put the smoking set within reach I shall be obliged."

Mrs. McSwat did so, and with her own fair hands she filled his new meerschaum, whose bowl was already taking a brownish tinge that gave promise of richer and grander result in the happy future.

"You don't know, Lobelia (puff). how gratefully I (puff) appreciate your (puff) kindness in interposing no objection to my indulgence in (puff, puff) this habit. Hard as would have been the sacrifice, Lobelia, I (puff) would have quit it cheerfully—that is to say (puff)—with comparative cheerfulness, if you had exacted it."

"How could I have asked you to quit smoking, Billiger," replied the young wife, "when you have never made the least objection to my chewing gum?"

Mr. McSwat laid the pipe down and looked at her in astonishment.

"Do you chew gum, Lobelia?" he said.　"I never suspected it."

"I—I confess I do sometimes, Billiger."

"Mrs. McSwat," said he, severely, "have you any idea of the consequences of inveterate gum chewing? Do you know the inconceivably vile materials of which the stuff is made?"

"It can't be any worse, Mr. Swatt, than the poisonous, filthy, reeking fumes of that dirty old pipe you are——"

"Lobelia McSwat, have a care! Don't provoke me too far, or——"

"Billiger McSwat, do you dare to threaten me? Don't glare and squint at me through that eye-glass till you have learned how to use it sir. You are——"

"Lobelia," exclaimed the young husband, pale with conflicting emotions, "you have spoken sneeringly of this meerschaum. It cost $25. But let that pass. I can bear it. To think, though, that the woman I have vowed to love and cherish," and his voice faltered—"upon whom I have poured out the treasure of a heart's richest affection, is a g-gum chew-chewer! O! O! Lo-be-lia!"

"B-Billiger!" sobbed Lobelia, "I'll qu-quit ch-chewing if you'll stop smoking!"

"I'll do it, my love!" he exclaimed.

His brow aflame with lofty and noble resolve, Billiger wrapped his smoking set, with pipe, tobacco and all, in a paper and threw the package to the remotest depths of a dark and gloomy attic on the topmost floor, while Lobelia gathered up all her wads of gum from their various hiding places, rolled them into a compact bundle and threw them into the attic likewise.

"With these slight sacrifices, Lobelia," said Billiger, tenderly, "we

propitiate the good angels of domestic bliss, and banish forever the
demon of discord from our hearthstone!"

* * * * * * *

Forty-eight hours had passed—48 short, happy hours. Night had
come again.

Billiger was in that attic. He had sneaked into it, and was fum-
bling around noiselessly for something. In the dark his hand had
come in contact with a shoe, and he grasped it. It had a foot in it.

There was a faint scream.

"Mrs. McSwat, is that you?"

"Mr. McSwat, it is."

"What are you doing here, madam?"

"Sir, I am looking for my gum. What are you doing here?"

"Madam, I am hunting for my pipe."

THE TELLTALE.

[With piping, merry tones try to suggest the notes of the bobolink in passages
where the bird is supposed to be speaking.]

ONCE on a golden afternoon,
  With radiant faces and hearts in tune,
    Two fond lovers in dreaming mood
    Threaded a rural solitude.
Wholly happy, they only knew
That the earth was bright and the sky was blue,
  That light and beauty and joy and song
  Charmed the way as they passed along;
The air was fragrant with woodland scents:
The squirrel frisked on the roadside fence;
  And hovering near them: "Chee—chee—Chink?"
  Queried the curious bobolink,
Pausing and peering with sidelong head,
As saucily questioning all they said;

While the ox-eye danced on its slender stem,
And all glad nature rejoiced with them.

Over the odorous fields were strewn
Wilting windrows of grass new-mown,
   And rosy billows of clover bloom
   Surged in the sunshine and breathed perfume.
Swinging low on the slender limb,
The sparrow warbled his wedding hymn,
   And, balancing on a blackberry brier,
   The bobolink sung with his heart on fire—
"Chink? If you wish to kiss her, do!
Do it, do it! You coward, you!
   Kiss her! Kiss—kiss her! Who will see?
   Only we three! we three! we three!"
Under garlands of drooping vines
Through dim vistas of sweet-breathed pines,
   Past wide meadow—fields, lately mowed,
   Wandered the indolent country road.

The lovers followed it, listing still,
And, loitering slowly, as lovers will,
   Entered a low-roofed bridge that lay
   Dusky and cool, in their pleasant way.
Under its arch a smooth brown stream
Silently glided, with glint and gleam,
   Shaded by graceful elms that spread
   Their verdurous canopy overhead,—
The stream so narrow, the boughs so wide,
They met and mingled across the tide.
   Alders loved it, and seemed to keep
   Patient watch as it lay asleep,
Mirroring clearly the trees and sky
And the fluttering form of the dragon-fly,

Save where the swift-winged swallow played
In and out in the sun and shade,
And darting and circling in merry chase,
Dipped, and dimpled its clear dark face.

Fluttering lightly from brink to brink,
Followed the garrulous bobolink,
  Rallying loudly, with mirthful din,
  The pair who lingered unseen within.
And when from the friendly bridge at last,
Into the road beyond they passed,
  Again beside them the tempter went,
  Keeping the thread of his argument:
"Kiss her—kiss her, chink a-chee-chee!
I'll not mention it, don't mind me;
  I'll be sentinel—I can see
  All around from this tall birch tree!"
But ah! they noted, nor deemed it strange,
In his rollicking chorus a trifling change:
  "Do it—do it!" with might and main,
  Warbled the tell-tale, " do it again!"

THE KNIGHT AND THE LADY.

[The exquisite humor of this selection should be made effective by a sprightly manner and a touch of comedy in expression.]

THE Lady Jane was tall and slim
      The Lady Jane was fair
  And Sir Thomas, her lord, was stout of limb,
  And his cough was short, and his eyes were dim,
  And he wore green "specs" with a tortoise shell rim,
  And his hat was remarkably broad in the brim,
  And she was uncommonly fond of him—
      And they were a loving pair!

13—S C.

And wherever they went, or wherever they came,
Every one hailed them with loudest acclaim;
  Far and wide,
  The people cried,
All sorts of pleasure, and no sort of pain,
To Sir Thomas the good, and the fair lady Jane!

Now Sir Thomas the good, be it well understood,
Was a man of very contemplative mood—
He would pore by the hour, o'er a weed or a flower,
Or the slugs, that came crawling out after a shower;
Black beetles, bumble-bees, blue-bottle flies,
And moths, were of no small account in his eyes;
An "industrious flea" he'd by no means despise,
While an "old daddy long-legs," whose long legs and thighs
Passed the common in shape, or in color, or size,
He was wont to consider an absolute prize.
Giving up, in short, both business and sport, he
Abandoned himself, *tout entier*, to philosophy.

Now as Lady Jane was tall and slim,
  And Lady Jane was fair,
And a good many years the junior of him,
There are some might be found entertaining a notion,
That such an entire and exclusive devotion
To that part of science, folks style entomology,
  Was a positive shame,
  And, to such a fair dame,
Really demanded some sort of apology;
Ever poking his nose into this, and to that—
At a gnat, or a bat, or a cat, or a rat,
At great ugly things, all legs and wings,
With nasty long tails, armed with nasty long stings;—

And eternally thinking, and blinking, and winking
At grubs—when he ought of *her* to he thinking.

But no! ah no! 'twas by no means so
    With the fair Lady Jane,
    Tout au contraire, no lady so fair,
Was e'er known to wear more contented an air;
And—let who would call—every day she was there
Propounding receipts for some delicate fare,
Some toothsome conserve, of quince, apple or pear,
Or distilling strong waters—or potting a hare—
Or counting her spoons and her crockery ware;
Enough to make less gifted visitors stare.

    Nay more; don't suppose
    With such doings as those
This account of her merits must come to a close;
No!—examine her conduct more closely, you'll find
She by no means neglected improving her mind;
For there all the while, with an air quite bewitching
She sat herring-boning, tambouring, or stitching,
Or having an eye to affairs of the kitchen.
    Close by her side,
    Sat her kinsman, MacBride—
Captain Dugald MacBride, Royal Scots Fusiliers;—
And I doubt if you'd find, in the whole of his clan,
A more highly intelligent, worthy young man;
    And there he'd be sitting,
    While she was a-knitting,
Reading aloud, with a very grave look,
Some very " wise saw," from some very good book—
    No matter who came,
    It was always the same,
The Captain was reading aloud to the dame,

Till, from having gone through half the books on the shelf,
They were *almost* as wise as Sir Thomas himself.

　　　Well, it happened one day—
　　　I really can't say
The particular month ;—but I *think* 'twas in May,
'Twas, I *know*, in the spring time, when " Nature looks gay,"
As the poet observes—and on tree-top and spray,
The dear little dickey birds carol away,
That the whole of the house was thrown into affright,
For no soul could conceive what was gone with the Knight.

　　　It seems he had taken
　　　A light breakfast--bacon,
An egg, a little broiled haddock—at most
A round and a half of some hot buttered toast,
With a slice of cold sirloin from yesterday's roast.
　　　But no matter for that—
　　　He had called for his hat,
With the brim that I've said was so broad and so flat,
And his " specs " with the tortoise shell rim, and his cane.
Thus armed he set out on a ramble—a-lack!

He *set out*, poor dear soul!—but he never came back!
　　　" First dinner bell " rang
　　　Out its euphonous clang
At five—folks kept early hours then—and the "last"
Ding-donged, as it ever was wont, at half-past.
Still the master was absent—the cook came and said, he
Feared dinner would spoil, having been so long ready,
That the puddings her ladyship thought such a treat
He was morally sure, would be scare fit to eat !
Said the lady, " Dish up ! Let the meal be served straight,
And let two or three slices be put on a plate,

And kept hot for Sir Thomas."—Captain Dugald **said grace,**
Then set himself down in Sir Thomas's place.

Wearily, wearily, all that night,
　　That live-long night, did the hours go **by;**
　　　　And the Lady Jane,
　　　　In grief and pain,
　　She sat herself down to cry!
　　　　And Captain MacBride,
　　　　Who sat by her side,
Though I really can't say that he actually **cried,**
　　At least had a tear in his eye!
As much as can well be expected, perhaps,
From "very young fellows" for "very old chaps."
　　　　And if he had said
　　　　What he'd got in the head,
'Twould have been " Poor old Buffer, he's certainly **dead!"**

The morning dawned—and the next—and the next,
And all in the mansion were still perplexed;
　　　　No knocker fell,
　　　　His approach to tell;
Not so much as a runaway ring at the bell.

Yet the sun shone bright upon tower and tree,
And the meads smiled green as green may be,
And the dear little dickey birds caroled with glee.
And the lambs in the park skipped merry and free.—
Without all was joy and harmony!

And thus 'twill be—nor long the day—
Ere we, like him, shall pass away!
Yon sun that now our bosoms warms,
Shall shine—but shine on other forms;

Yon grove, whose choir so sweetly cheers
Us now, shall sound on other ears;
The joyous lambs, as now, shall play,
But other eyes their sports survey;
The stream we loved shall roll as fair,
The flowery sweets, the trim parterre,
Shall scent, as now, the ambient air;
The tree whose bending branches bear
The one loved name—shall yet be there—
But where the hand that carved it?　Where?

   These were hinted to me as the very ideas
Which passed through the mind of the fair Lady Jane,
As she walked on the esplanade to and again,
   With Captain MacBride,
   Of course at her side,
Who could not look *quite* so forlorn—though he tried.
An "idea," in fact, had got into *his* head,
That if "poor dear Sir Thomas" should really be dead,
It might be no bad "spec" to be there in his stead,
And by simply contriving, in due time, to wed
   A lady who was young and fair,
   A lady slim and tall,
To set himself down in comfort there,
   The lord of Tapton Hall.

   Thinks he, " We have sent
   Half over Kent,
And nobody knows how much money's been spent,
Yet no one's been found to say which way he went!
Here's a fortnight and more has gone by, and we've tried
Every plan we could hit on—and had him well cried,
   ' MISSING!! *Stolen or Strayed,*
   Lost or Mislaid,

A GENTLEMAN ;—middle-aged, sober and staid ;
Stoops slightly ;—and when he left home was arrayed
In a sad colored suit, somewhat dingy and frayed ;
Had spectacles on with a tortoise-shell rim,
And a hat rather low crowned, and broad in the brim.
> Whoe'er shall bear,
> Or send him with care,
(Right side uppermost) home ; or shall give notice where
The middle-aged GENTLEMAN is ; or shall state
Any fact, that may tend to throw light on his fate,
To the man at the turnpike, called *Tappington Gate*,
Shall receive a reward of *Five Pounds* for his trouble
N. B —If defunct, the *Reward* will be double !!'

> " Had he been above ground,
> He *must* have been found.
No ; doubtless he's shot—or he's hanged—or he's drowned!
> Then his widow—ay ! ay !
> But what will folks say?
To address her at once, at so early a day !
Well—what then—who cares !—let 'em say what they may.'
> When a man has decided,
> As Captain MacBride did,
And one fully made up his mind on the matter, he
Can't be too prompt in unmasking his battery.
He began on the instant, and vowed that her eyes
Far exceeded in brilliance the stars in the skies ;
That her lips were like roses, her cheeks were like lilies·
Her breath had the odor of daffadowndillies !—
With a thousand more compliments, equally true,
Expressed in similitudes equally new !
> Then his left arm he placed
> Around her jimp, taper waist—
Ere she fixed to repulse or return his embrace,

Up came running a man at a deuce of a pace,
With that very pecular expression of face
Which always betokens dismay or disaster,
Crying out—'twas the gard'ner—" Oh, ma'am we've found
        master ! ! "
" Where? where? " screamed the lady; and echo screamed,
        " Where? "
        The man couldn't say " there! "
        He had no breath to spare,
But gasping for breath he could only respond
By pointing—he pointed, alas!—TO THE POND.
'Twas e'en so; poor dear Knight, with his " specs " and his hat,
He'd gone poking his nose into this and to that;
When close to the side of the bank, he espied
An uncommon fine tadpole, remarkably fat!
        He stooped;—and he thought her
        His own;—he had caught her!
Got hold of her tail—and to land almost brought her,
When—he plumped head and heels into fifteen feet water!

The Lady Jane was tall and slim,
        The Lady Jane was fair,
Alas! for Sir Thomas !—she grieved for him,
As she saw two serving men sturdy of limb,
        His body between them bear :
She sobbed and she sighed, she lamented and cried,
        For of sorrow brimful was her cup;
She swooned, and I think she'd have fallen down and died,
        If Captain MacBride
        Hadn't been by her side
With the gardener ;—they both their assistance supplied,
        And managed to hold her up.
          But when she " comes to,"
          Oh! 'tis shocking to view

The sight which the corpse reveals !
    Sir Thomas' body,
    It looked so odd—he
Was half eaten up by the eels !

    His waitcoast and hose,
    And the rest of his clothes,
Were all gnawed through and through ;
    And out of each shoe,
    An eel they drew ;
And from each of his pockets they pulled out **two,**
And the gardener himself had secreted a few,
    As well might be supposed he'd do,
For, when he came running to give the alarm,
He had six in the basket that hung on his arm.

Good Father John was summoned anon ;
Holy water was sprinkled and little bells tinkled,
    And tapers were lighted,
    And incense ignited,
And masses were sung, and masses were said,
All day, for the quiet repose of the dead,
And all night no one thought about going to bed.

But Lady Jane was tall and slim,
    And Lady Jane was fair,
And ere morning came, that winsome dame
Had made up her mind, or—what's much the same—
Had *thought about*, once more " changing her name,"
    And she said with a pensive air,
To Thompson the valet, while taking away,
When supper was over, the cloth and the tray,
"Eels a many I've ate ; but any

So good ne'er tasted before !—
They're a fish, too, of which I'm remarkably fond—
Go—pop Sir Thomas again in the pond—
Poor dear !—*he'll catch us some more.*"

MORAL.

All middle-aged gentlemen, let me advise,
If you're married, and haven't got very good eyes,
Don't go poking about after blue-bottle flies.
If you've spectacles, don't have a tortoise-shell rim
And don't go near the water—unless you can swim.

Married ladies, especially such as are fair,
Tall and slim, I would next recommend to beware,
How, on losing one spouse, they give way to despair;
But let them reflect, there are fish, and no doubt on't,
As good *in* the river, as ever came *out* on't.

RICHARD HARRIS BARHAM.

JIMMY BROWN'S SISTER'S WEDDING.

SUE ought to have been married a long while ago. That's what everybody says who knows her. She has been engaged to Mr. Travers for three years, and has had to refuse lots of offers to go to the circus with other young men. I have wanted her to get married, so that I could go and live with her and Mr. Travers. When I think that if it hadn't been for a mistake I made she would have been married yesterday, I find it dreadfully hard to be resigned. But we ought always to be resigned to everything when we can't help it.

Before I go any further I must tell about my printing press. It belonged to Tom McGinnis, but he got tired of it and sold it to me real cheap. He was going to exchange it for a bicycle, a St. Bernard dog, and twelve good books, but he finally let me have it for a dollar and a half.

It prints beautifully, and I have printed cards for ever so many people, and made three dollars and seventy cents already. I thought it would be nice to be able to print circus bills in case Tom and I should ever have another circus, so I sent to the city and bought some type more than an inch high, and some beautiful yellow paper.

Last week it was finally agreed that Sue and Mr. Travers should be married without waiting any longer. You should have seen what a state of mind she and mother were in. They did nothing but buy new clothes, and sew, and talk about the wedding all day long. Sue was determined to be married in church, and to have six bridemaids and six bridegrooms, and flowers and music and all sorts of things. The only thing that troubled her was making up her mind whom to invite. Mother wanted her to invite Mr. and Mrs. McFadden and the seven McFadden girls, but Sue said they had insulted her, and she couldn't bear the idea of asking the McFadden tribe.

Everybody agreed that old Mr. Wilkinson, who once came to a party at our house with one boot and one slipper, couldn't be invited; but it was decided that every one else that was on good terms with our family should have an invitation.

Sue counted up all the people she meant to invite, and there was nearly three hundred of them. You would hardly believe it, but she told me that I must carry around all the invitations and deliver them myself. Of course, I couldn't do this without neglecting my studies and losing time, which is always precious, so I thought of a plan which would save Sue the trouble of directing three hundred invitations and save me from wasting time in delivering them.

I got to work with my printing-press, and printed a dozen splendid big bills about the wedding. When they were printed I cut a lot of small pictures of animals and ladies riding on horses out of some old circus bills and pasted them on the wedding bills. They were perfectly gorgeous, and you could see them four or five rods off. When they were all done I made some paste in a tin pail, and went out after dark and pasted them in good places all over the village.

The next afternoon father came into the house looking very stern, and carrying one of the wedding bills in his hand.   He handed it to Sue and said: " Susan, what does this mean ?   These bills are posted all over the village, and there are crowds of people reading them." Sue read the bill, and then she gave an awful shriek, and fainted away, and I hurried down to the post-office to see if the mail had come in.   This is what was on the wedding bills, and I am sure it was spelled all right :

Miss Susan Brown announces that she will marry
Mr. James Travers
at the Church next Thursday, at half-past seven, sharp.
All the Friends of the Family
With the exception of
the McFadden tribe and old Mr. Wilkinson
are invited.
Come early and bring
Lots of Flowers.

Now what was there to find fault with in that ?   It was printed beauti-fully, and every word was spelled right, with the exception of the name of the church, and I didn't put that in, because I wasn't quite sure how to spell it.   The bill saved Sue all the trouble of sending out invitations, and it said everything that anybody would want to know about the wedding.   Any other girl but Sue would have been pleased, and would have thanked me for all my trouble, but she was as angry as if I had done something real bad.   Mr. Travers was almost as angry as Sue, and it was the first time he was ever angry with me.   I am afraid now that he won't let me ever come and live with him.   He hasn't said a word about my coming since the wedding bills were put up.   As for the wedding, it has been put off, and Sue says she will go to New York to be married, for she would die if she were to have a wedding at home after that boy's dreadful conduct.   What is worse, I am to be sent away to boarding-school, and all because I made a mis-take in printing the wedding bills without first asking Sue how she would like to have them printed.

YE OLDE TYME TAYLE OF Ye KNIGHTE, Ye YEOMANNE, AND Ye FAIRE DAMOSEL.

[This is a fine example of the mock-heroic, and should be read in a rollicking, grandiloquent manner. Pronounce the words as written.]

CANTO I.

ONCE on a time there was a knight,
    Was called Sir Dominoes
Johannes Houven-Gouven-Schnouvers
    San Domingo Mose—
A warrior he of noble blood
    As e'er found fun in fight.
Oh, when he put his armor on
    He was a fearsome sight!
Bound round with straps, and strips, and strings,
    With thingumbobs and pegs,
With stove-lids buckled on his breast,
    And stove-pipes on his legs,
An iron pot upon his head,
    A brazen horn to toot,
A sword stuck up his burly back,
    A razor down his boot.

He owned great castles, lands, and men,
    And gallant ships, and steeds,
And twice as many golden coins
    As anybody needs.
Ye knight he loved a farmer's lass:
    Alas! she loved not him;
But doted on a yeo-man bold,
    By name Sam-u-el Slimme,
Who ploughed, and sowed, and reaped, and binned,
    Who staunchly tilled ye dirt,

And wore a look of honesty,
　　Likewise a flannel shirt.
Strong was his arm; warm was his heart;
　　Cold was his common-sense;
But, otherwise, poor Sam-u-el
　　Had not a dozen pence.

Yet Albacinda scoffed and scorned
　　Ye high and haughty knight:
She did not like his iron clothes,
　　Nor care to see him fight.
His castle was too old and dark;
　　She scorned his gold as well—
Her father on Sir Mose did smile:
　　She clung to Sam-u-el.

CANTO II.

One morning in ye month of May,
　　Amidst ye growing grain,
Ye rival lovers met, eftsoon,
　　A-coming down ye lane.
"Give way, vile caitiff!" cried Sir Mose,
　　"And let me journey on;
Or I will strew thy fragments up
　　And down ye horizon!"

Then bold Sir Mose he drew his sword,
　　Felt once its rusty edge,
And slashed a slash at Sam-u-el
　　That mowed ten yards of hedge.
I' faith!　It was a vicious blow
　　And whistled in ye air!
But when it reached brave Sam-u-el,
　　Sam-u-el was not there.

So fierce and fearful was ye stroke
    Sir What's-his-name arose,
Turned three successive summersaults,
    And landed on his nose.
His stove-plates drove him in ye mud
    Six inches by ye fall:
Ye knight, so weightily got up.
    Could not get up at all.

Sam-u-el did not haste away,
    For he had cut a stick
Four times as long as his right arm,
    And e'en a'most as thick;
Then, though ye knight was well dressed up,
    Ye farmer dressed him down,
He made ye knight so black and blue
    He was quite done up brown.
"Ye picked this bed," quoth Sam-u-el,
    " Methinks I'll let thee lie :
Thy lying once will be grim truth.
    Sweet dreams, fair sir! Good-by!"
Ye knight, so sorely taken in,
    Would fain be taken out ;
" I stick at this! " in wrath he cried,
    And loud for help did shout.

And eke he sware a mighty vow,
    "Great fishing-hooks, y' bet,
By my best Sunday garter-strings,
    I'll beat ye plough-man yet !"
His hair it stood straight up for rage;
    His lips were white with foam ;
He sware to go that night and burn
    Sam-u-el's humble home.

CANTO III.

Above ye deep and danksome dell
    Beneath ye gloomy wood,
Ye wind it howled a dismal strain,
    Ye knight he howled for blood;
But as he stole along, a bull
    Espied ye lantern dim,
And whilst he hunted Sam-u-el,
    Ye bull it hunted him!
When it flew in, ye light flew out;
    Ye knight flew, with a cry;
His coat-tails they flew out behind;
    His legs how they did fly!
Ye stove-pipes flew; ye stove-lids, too;
    His weapons went to pot;
Sir Mose arose upon his toes:
    He just got up and got!

With those great horns, three cloth-yards long
    A whistling in ye wind,
So on ye knight sped, like some cur
    With a tin can behind.
For e'en a'most two miles he fled;
    Nigh tuckered out was he,
When out of danger's way he clomb
    Into an apple-tree,
Whereon he hung a-shivering
    And shrieking at ye beast,
Till Sam-u-el came out to work,
    When day dawned in ye east.

Forsooth, Sam-u-el's rage waxed hot;
    Then loud he 'gan to laugh:

SOLDIER-GIRL COSTUME

"MAY WITH BLOSSOMS STOPS THE WAY."

"To judge by thy companion, sir,
    Thou art a bawling calf—
For men are known, I trow, sir, by
    Ye company they keep—
Though only chickens roost in trees
    Whilst honest people sleep!"
Sir Mose yelled fiercely; but, quite weak
    From hanging all ye night,
He fell upon ye bull, which tossed
    Him clean up out of sight!

Canto IV.

Then up gat bold young Sam-u-el
    And galloped down ye lane,
Unto his true-love's window-ledge,
    And tapped upon ye pane:
"Come forth, sweet-heart; my love thou art!
    Come forth and hie away!
Thou'lt married be, dear girl, to me,
    Before high noon this day.
Sweet Albacinda, fly with me
    And rule these vast concerns
Held safe in trust for bold Sir Mose!
    (If ever he returns!)"

Now gallop, gallop, gallant horse!
    Now gallop with thy prize!
And hurl ye clay in chuncks away
    As big as apple-pies!
Fly down ye road, around ye hill,
    Up to ye castle door;
Across ye trembling drawbridge fly
    Up to ye banquet floor!

14—S. C.

Quick, call ye gray-haired friar in
   From out his gloomy cell,
To tie these two young true-loves tight!
   Ring out, ye marriage bell!
Ring "jingle-jangle jangle jing!"
   Ring "fol-de-riddle-lay!"
Bold Sam-u-el has won his bride
   For ever and a day!
Go, bid ye foolish father
   To forget his angry pride,
Accept his new-made son-in-law,
   And bless ye bonnie bride.

                              JACK BENNETT.

THE SOFT GUITAR.

SCENE: Moonlight.   Beneath the lady's window appeareth the lover with guitar

Locate the lady's window to the right.   When she replies let her speak toward
                              the left.]

OPEN thy lattice, O lady bright!
   The earth lies calm in the fair moonlight;
   Gaze on the glint of each glancing star,
   And list to the notes of my soft guitar.

At the lady's window a vision shone—
'Twas the lady's head with a night-cap on.

See! at the casement appearing now,
With lily fingers she hides her brow.
Oh, weep not—though bitter thy sorrows are,
I will soothe them to rest with my soft guitar.

Then the lady answered, "Who's going to weep?
Go 'way with your fiddle, and let me sleep."

Then sleep, dear lady; thy fringed lids close,
Pinions of cherubim fan thy repose,
While through thy casement, slightly ajar,
Steal the sweet notes of my soft guitar.

Then the lady her " secret pain " confessed
With the plaintive murmur, " Oh, give us a rest."

Chide me not harshly, O lady fair!
Bend from thy lattice and hear my prayer.
Sighing for thee, I wander afar,
Mournfully touching my soft guitar.

And the lady answered : "You stupid thing,
If you've got the catarrh, stop trying to sing!"

Cruel, but fair one, thy scorn restrain!
Better death's quiet than thy disdain.
I go to fall in some distant war,
Bearing in battle my loved guitar.

Answered the lady: "Well, hurry and go!
I'm holding the slop-basin ready to throw."

False one, I leave thee! When I'am at rest
Still shall my memory haunt thy breast;
A spectral vision thy joy shall mar—
A skeleton playing a soft guitar!

And the lady cried, in a scornful tone,
"Old skeleton, go it—and play it *alone!*"

Then the lover in agony roamed afar—
Fell drunk in the gutter and smashed his guitar.

                                    P. H BOWNE.

A RECEIPT FOR A RACKET.

WHAT does it take to make a racket?
 Well, bless me, I certainly ought to know,
 For I have made them a score of times or so!
Here's the receipt—and I can't be wrong—
For making them hot and sweet and strong!

What does it take to make a racket?
Two small boys in pants and jacket;
An empty room and a bare wood floor;
A couple of sticks to bang the door;
A chair or two to break and to swing;
A trumpet to blow and a bell to ring:
A stamp and a tramp like a great big man;
And, when you can get it, an old tin pan;
A flight of stairs for a climb and a tumble;
A nursery maid to growl and grumble;
A chorus of howl and cry and shriek
To drown your voice if you try to speak;
A dozen good blows on knees and back,
Each one coming down with a terrible whack;
A couple of falls that would crack a nut,
And one good bump on your occiput;
A rush and a scurry, a tear and a clatter,
A mamma to cry " Now, what is the matter? "
And take these, and shake these, and put in a packet,
And you'll have just the jolliest kind of a racket!

Of course, I am bound to confess
You can manage to make it with less,
(For this is a regular rich receipt,
For pudding and sauce and all complete),
 And still have a very good show
 If you follow directions below:

You can leave out the room and the floor,
The bumps and the bangs on the door;
The bell and the sticks and the stairs;
The trumpets, the howls and the chairs;
The whack and the fall and the rise;
The shrieks and the groans and the cries;
Mamma and the pan and the tramp,
The nurse and the growl and the stamp,—
But one thing you must have, however you get it;
Or else, if you don't, you will surely regret it—
For remember my words—if you happen to lack it
You never can have the least bit of a racket—
And that is, two small boys in pants and in jacket!

SHACOB'S LAMENT.

OXCOOSE me if I shed some tears,
    Und wipe my nose away;
    Und if a lump vos in my troat,
        It comes up dere to shtay.

My sadness I shall now unfoldt,
    Und if dot tale of woe
Don'd do some Dutchmans any good,
    Den I don't pelief I know.

You see, I fall myself in love,
    Und effery night I goes
Across to Brooklyn by dot pridge,
    All dressed in Sunday clothes.

A vidder vomans vos der brize,
    Her husband he vos dead;
Und all alone in this coldt vorldt
    Dot vidder vos, she said.

Her heart for love vos on der pine,
  Und dot I like to see;
Und all der time I hoped dot heart
  Vos on der pine for me.

I keeps a butcher shop, you know,
  Und in a stocking stout,
I put avay my gold and bills,
  Und no one gets him oudt.

If in der night some bank cashier
  Goes skipping off mit cash,
I shleep so sound as nefer vos,
  Vhile rich folks go to shmash.

I court dot vidder sixteen months.
  Dot vidder she courts me,
Und vhen I says: "Vill you be mine?"
  She says: "You bet I'll be!"

Ve vos engaged—oh! blessed fact!
  I squeeze dot dimpled hand;
Her head upon my shoulder lays,
  Shust like a bag of sand.

"Before der vedding day vos set,"
  She vispers in mine ear,
"I like to say I haf to use
  Some cash, my Jacob, dear.

"I owns dis house and two big farms,
  Und ponds and railroad stock;
Und up in Yonkers I bosses
  A grand big peesness block.

"Der times vos dull, my butcher boy,
    Der market vos no good,
Und if I sell "—I squeezed her handt
    To show I understood.

Next day—oxcoose my briny tears—
    Dot shtocking took a shrink;
I counted out twelve hundred in
    Der cleanest kind o' chink.

Und later, by two days or more,
    Dot vidder shlopes avay;
Und leaves a note behindt for me
    In vhich dot vidder say:

"DEAR SHAKE:

        Der rose vos redt,
            Der violet blue—
        You see I've left,
            Und you're left, too!"

BE BRAVE.

WHEN sudden cry shall rend the air,
    That hardest heart would move,
Be ready then to rush to her,
    Your gallantry to prove,
When her eyes dilate with horror,
    And her cheek doth pale with fear,
And you think that some torpedo
    Has exploded very near,
Do not send for some quack doctor,
    Nor for a vinaigrette,

But seize some deadly weapon—
    The nearest you can get,
And fiercely let it fly,
    Exclaiming, "There, thou monster!
'Tis now thy fate to die!"
    When her tones so very grateful
Will repay you for your care,
    As she murmurs, "You are very brave,
I really must declare!"
    And when her friends have gathered round,
Join not in their reproach,
    As they in dire amazement find
'Twas a terrible cock roach.

                        MAY COOPER.

HE TRIED TO TELL HIS WIFE.

IF there is one thing more than another calculated to throw a man into a gnashing-of-the teeth and tearing-of-the hair condition, it is his attempt to give the wife of his bosom an account of some ordinary affair.   He begins with:

Oh, my dear, I must tell you something Jack Burroughs told me to-day while ——

Where did you see Jack Burroughs? answered the wife.

Oh, we went to luncheon together, and ——

How did you happen to go to luncheon together?

Well, we didn't exactly go out together. I met Jack at the restaurant, and ——

What restaurant?

Calloway's, and Jack ——

How did you happen to go to Calloway's? I thought you always lunched at Draper's?

I nearly always do, but I just happened to drop into Calloway's to-day, along with Jack, and ——

Does he always lunch at Calloway's?

I'm sure, my dear, that I don't know if he does or not. It makes no earthly difference if ——

Oh, of course not. I just wondered if he did, that's all. Go on with your story.

Well, while we were eating our soup, Jack ——

What kind of soup?

Oxtail. Jack said that ——

I thought you disliked oxtail soup?

Well, I don't care much about it, but ——

How did you happen to order it if you didn't care for it?

Because I *did*. But the soup has nothing to do with the story.

Oh, of course not. I never said that it did. I don't see why you should get cross over a simple question. Go on.

Well, while we were eating our soup, Lawrence Hildreth and his wife came in, and ——

They did?

I have just said so.

Well, you needn't be so cross about it.

They came in, and ——

Is she pretty?

Pretty enough. Jack bowed, and ——

Does he know them?

Well, now, do you suppose he would have bowed if he hadn't known them? I declare if I ——

How was she dressed?

How should I know? I never looked at her dress. What I was going to tell you was that ——

Did they sit near you?

Yes, at the next table. And while they were ordering Jack said that they ——

Couldn't they hear him?

Do you suppose that Jack would have no more sense than to let them hear him talking about them? Look here, now ——

James, if you can't tell a simple little incident without getting into a passion, you'd better keep it to yourself.   What did Jack say?

He said that Mrs. Hildreth's father was opposed to the match, and ——

How did he know that?

Great Cæsar!   There you go again!

James, you will please remember that it is your wife to whom you are speaking, sir!

No other woman could drive me raving, distracted, crazy, asking silly questions about ——

James!

Every time I try to tell you anything you begin, and you ——

James I do not propose listening to any such insulting remarks, and ——

You never listen to anything.   That's the trouble.   If ——

When I ask you a simple question you ——

I'd say "simple!"   You've asked me a million simple questions in the last half hour, just because I was going to tell you that Jack Burroughs said that ——

I do not wish to know what Mr. Jack Burroughs said, if you cannot tell it respectfully.   I shall have my dinner sent to my room, since it is so painful for you to eat with an idiot!

And the much-injured wife retires scornfully, while her husband narrowly escapes an attack of apoplexy.

———

A RUSSIAN COURTSHIP.

"BE mine," said the ardent young Sawmilegoff,
　　　In a voice with emotion quite husky,
　　"My fondest devotion, oh, please do not scoff,
　　　Katina Pojakaroulski!"

"Techernyschevsky, my friend," the shy maiden replied,
　　"Your people are noble and rich.

Would a Golgusoff's granddaughter be a fit bride
    For a nephew of Maximovitch?"

'I care not a kopeck!" he said. " In my droshky
    I have you safe now, and I laugh
At the wealth of a Klitkin or Overhauloshki,
    Gojavnik, or Pullerzedoff.

"You are worth more to me than the gold of Slugmiski,
    Brakemupski, or Sumarakoff!
Katina Pojakaroulski, it's risky,
    But I'm going to carry you off!"

And this is the way young Sawmilegoff
    Put an end to all further discussion,
'Twas a simpler proceeding to carry her off
    Than to go on courting in Russian.

—————

PAT'S LOVE LETTER.

IT'S Patrick Dolin, myself and no other,
    That's after informin' you without any bother,
    That your own darlin' self has put me heart in a blaze
And made me your sweetheart the rest of me days.
And now I sits down to write ye this letter,
To tel' how I loves ye, as none can love better.
Mony's the day, sure, since first I got smitten
Wid yer own purty face, that's bright as a kitten's,
And yer illegant figger, that's just the right size;
Faith! I'm all over in love wid ye, clear up till me eyes.
You won't think me desavin', or tellin' a lie,
If I tell who's in love wid me, just ready to die.
There's Bridget McCregan, full of coketish tricks,

Keeps flatterin' me pride, to get me heart in a fix:
And Bridget, you know, has great expectations
From her father that's dead, and lots of relations.
Then there's Biddy O'Farrel, the cunningest elf,
Sings "Patrick, me darlin'," and that means meself.
I might marry them both, if I felt so inclined,
But there's no use talking of the likes of their kind.
I trates them both alike, without impartiality,
And maintains meself sure on the ground of neutrality
On me knees, Helen, darlint, I ask your consent
"For better or worse," without asking a cent.
I'd do anything in the world—anything you would say,
If you'd be Mistress Dolin instead of Miss Day.
I'd save all me money and buy me a house,
Where nothing should tease us so much as mouse;
And you'll hear nothing else from year out to year in,
But swate words of kindness from Patrick Dolin.
Then—if ye should die—forgive me the thought,
I'd always behave as a dacent man ought.
I'd spend all me days in wailing and crying
And wish for nothin' so much as jist to be dying.
Then you'd see on marble slabs, reared up side by side,
"Here lies Patrick Dolin, and Helen, his bride."
Yer indulgence, in conclusion, on me letter I ask,
For to write a love letter is no aisy task;
I've an impediment in me speech, as me letter shows,
And a cold in me head makes me write through me nose.
Please write me a letter, in me great-uncle's care,
With the prescription upon it, "Patrick Dolin, Esquare."
"In haste," write in big letters, on the outside of the cover,
And believe me forever, your distractionate lover.
        Written wid me own hand.

                                    his
                        PATRICK X DOLIN
                                   mark.

MY NEIGHBOR'S CALL.

I DON'T want to compel you
  To let your baking go,
But I came in to tell you
  Some things you ought to know!

It won't take long; no doubt you
  Will think it can't be so,
But folks all talk about you!
  I've come to let you know.

Now there's your next door neighbor—
  Don't say I told you, though!
She says its no great labor
  To find out all you know!

You see you're too confiding;
  You don't know friend from foe.
I'll set you right, providing
  You think you ought to know.

You've heard of Mrs. Grundy?
  She thinks it looks quite low
For you to drive out Sunday.
  I'm sure you ought to know:

Your class don't like their teacher.
  I knew it long ago!
They all prefer Miss Preacher—
  Thought you might like to know.

You must change your dressmaker;
  You make a sorry show
Primmed up like some old Quaker!
  I s'pose you didn't know.

But then I've heard it hinted
   You don't pay what you owe;
I suppose your means are stinted.
   Of course you ought to know.

Though you may not concede it,
   Your baby doesn't grow!
They say you don't half feed it—
   But then you ought to know.

I saw your husband last night
   With Mrs. So and So;
Of course it may be all right,
   But I should want to know.

I think this bread will sour,
   You don't half mix your dough;
I mould mine just an hour—
   It's strange you shouldn't know!

You need me to propel you!
   This clock's a little slow—
I'll drop in soon and tell you
   More things you ought to know!

GEORGIA A. PECK.

A WOMAN'S WATCH.

OH, I am a woman's watch, am I,
   But I would that I were not;
   For if you knew, you would not deny
That mine is a sorry lot.
She'll let me rest for a great long while,
   Then all of a sudden seek
To twist me up so tight that I'll
   Keep going for a week.

She leaves me open when she will,
Till I'm sick of dirt and things;
Of pins and hair I have got my fill,
And of buttons, hooks and strings.
There's a four-leaf clover in me, too,
And a piece of a photograph;
I'm stuffed completely through and through
With toothpicks, cloves and chaff.

My hands are twisted to and fro,
I'm thumped and jarred, alack!
And then, if I fail to straightway go,
I'm pounded front and back.
With her hat-pin all my wheels she'll pry,
Till she breaks them, every one,
And then she'll say: "I don't see why
This mean old thing won't run!"

AN INCOMPLETE REVELATION.

[The figures refer to the corresponding numbers in Part I.]

WHILE Quaker folks were Quakers still, some fifty years ago,
    When coats were drab and gowns were plain and speech was
        staid and slow,
Before Dame Fashion dared suggest a single friz or curl,
There dwelt, mid Penfield's[2] peaceful shades, an old-time Quaker girl.

Ruth Wilson's garb was of her sect. Devoid[4] of furbelows,
She spoke rebuke[15] to vanity from bonnet to her toes;
Sweet redbird was she, all disguised in feathers of the dove,
With dainty foot and perfect form and eyes that dreamt of love.

Sylvanus Moore, a bachelor of forty years or so,
A quaintly pious, weazened soul, with beard and hair of tow

And queer thin legs, and shuffling walk and drawling, nasal tone,
Was prompted by the Spirit to make[2] this maid his own.

He knew it was the Spirit, for he felt it in his breast
As oft before in meeting-time, and, sure of his request,
Procured the permit in due form. On Fourth-day of that week
He let Ruth know the message true that he was moved to speak.

"Ruth, it has been revealed[3] to me that thee and I shall wed,
I have spoken to the meeting and the members all have said
That our union seems a righteous one[1], which they will not gainsay,
So if convenient to thy view, I'll wed thee[7] next Third-day."

The cool possession of herself by Friend Sylvanus Moore
Aroused her hot[14] resentment, which by effort she forbore—
She knew he was a goodly man, of simple, childlike mind—
And checked the word "Impertinence!" and answered him in kind:

'Sylvanus Moore, do thee go home[15] and wait until I see
The fact that I must be thy wife revealéd unto *me*."
And thus she left him there alone, at will to[12] ruminate—
More puzzled[17] at the mysteries of love, free-will, and fate.

RICHARD A. JACKSO.

WHEN SAM'WEL LED THE SINGIN'.

OF course I love the house o' God,
    But I don't feel to hum there
The way I uster do, afore
    New-fangled ways had come there.
Though things are finer now a heap,
    My heart it keeps a-clingin'
To our big, bare old meetin'-house,
    Where Sam'wel led the singin'.

I 'low it's sorter solemn-like
    To hear the organ pealin';
It kinder makes yer blood run cold,
    An' fills ye full o' feeling.
But, somehow, it don't tech the spot—
    Now, mind ye, I ain't slingin'
No slurs—ez that bass viol did
    When Sam'wel led the singin'.

I tell ye what, when he struck up
    The tune, an' sister Hanner
Put in her purty treble—eh?
    That what you'd call sopranner—
Why, all the choir, with might an' main,
    Set to, an' seemed a-flingin'
Ther hull souls out with ev'ry note,
    When Sam'wel led the singin'.

An', land alive, the way they'd race
    Through grand old " Coronation!"
Each voice a chasin' t'other round,
    It jes' beat all creation!
I allus thought it must 'a' set
    The bells o' heaven a ringin'
To hear us " Crown Him Lord of All,"
    When Sam'wel led the singin'.

Folks didn't sing for money then!
    They sung because 'twas in 'em
An' must come out. I useter feel—
    If Parson couldn't win 'em
With preachin' an' with prayin' an'
    His everlastin' dingin'—
That choir'd fetch sinners to the fold,
    When Sam'wel led the singin'.

15—S. C

OBSERVATIONS BY REV. GABE TUCKER.

YOU may notch it on de palin's as a mighty resky plan
　　To make your judgment by the clo'es dat kivers up a
　　man;
For I hardly needs to tell you how you often come ercross
A fifty-dollar saddle on a twenty-dollar hoss.
An', walkin' in de low groun's, you diskiver, as you go,
Dat the fines' shuck may hide de meanes' nubbin in a row!
I think a man has got a mighty slender chance for heben
Dat holds on to his piety but one day out o' seben;
Dat talks about de sinners wid a heap o' solemn chat,
An' nebber draps a nickel in de missionary hat;
Dat's foremost in the meetin' house for raisin all de chunes,
But lays aside his 'ligion wid his Sunday pantaloons!

J. A. Macon.

MR. EISSELDORF AND THE WATER PIPE.

'HANS, dot vater pipe giffs no vater alretty, und you vos petter
　　sent oop dot blumber to vix id vonce more."

This remark was addressed to a highly respected German
citizen as he sat in front of his cosy grate. He received the announce-
ment with evident disfavor.

"Vot! Dot vater pipe again! I vas shoost congratulatin' meinself
dot de ice vagon comes no more, und dot new hat vos paid for, und
dot Christmas vas a long vays ahead—und now von off dose blumbers! Mein gracious, Gretchen! I got no money for blumbers.
I vixes id myself." "Joe!" addressing his ten-year-old son, "vere vas
dot leak?"

Then Joe proceeded to explain that the leak was under the house,
where the stout frame of his worthy ancestor could hardly go.

"Neffer mind, neffer mind. You gets me some bipe und a monkey
wrench, und I save dot blumber's bill.

So the next day Joe got the pipe and the monkey wrench, and his father, having divested himself of all surplus garments, entered the hole, pulling the pipe after him.   It was a tight squeeze, and after laying on his back to convenience his position, he proceeded to discover the leak. Very little water was now coming from it, as he had taken the precaution to turn off the tap.   He hadn't turned it quite tight enough and yelled : "Turn off de vater."

"All righdt, fader," replied Joe.

Joe didn't know his right hand from his left, nor the philosophy of screws, and turned it on.

The old gentleman's mouth was under the leak.   He was wedged in.   He sputtered and swore and swore and sputtered, but his wild yells to Joe were muffled by the sound of deluging water and Joe was intent on a dog-fight across the way, as he sat on an empty nail keg and chewed gum.

He looked over his shoulder and saw the old man with a shining red face, mud-bespattered, angrily creeping from the hole.   His clothes clung limply to him and trickling streams meandered down his neck.

Joe apprehended danger and dashed away at a pace that left his corpulent father far in the rear.   As the boy sped out of sight Mr. Eisseldorf gathered himself with a supreme effort and hurled the monkey-wrench at the fleeing form, crying :

"Mine cracious, do you dink I vas a duck ? "

THE WATERMILLION.

THERE was a watermillion
　　Growing on a vine,
And there were a pickanniny
　　A-watching it all the time.

And when that watermillion
　　Were a-ripening in the sun,
And the stripes along its jacket
　　Were coming one by one,

That pickaninny hooked it,
And toting it away,
He ate that entire million
Within one single day.

He ate the rind and pieces,
He finished it with vim—
And then that watermillion
Just up and finished him.

AN ALL=ROUND INTELLECTUAL MAN.

HE was up in mathematics,
Had a taste for hydrostatics,
And could talk about astronomy from Aristarchus down;
He could tell what kind of beans
Were devoured by the Chaldeans,
And he knew the date of every joke made by a circus clown.

He was versed in evolution,
And would instance the poor Russian
As a type of despotism in the modern age of man.
He could write a page of matter
On the different kinds of batter
Used in making flinty gimcracks on the modern cooking plan.

He could revel in statistics,
He was well up in the fistics,
Knew the pedigree of horses dating 'way back from the ark.
Far and wide his tips were quoted,
And his base-ball stuff was noted.
In political predictions he would always hit the mark.

He could write upon the tariff,
And he didn't seem to care if
He was called off to review a book or write a poem or two:
He could boil down stuff and edit,
Knew the value of a credit,
And could hustle with the telegraph in a style excelled by few.

He could tell just how a fire
Should be handled ; as a liar
He was sure to exercise a wise, discriminative taste.
He was mild and yet undaunted,
And no matter what was wanted
He was always sure to get it first, yet never was in haste.

But despite his reputation
As a brainy aggregation,
He was known to be deficient in a manner to provoke,
For no matter when you met him
He would borrow if you let him,
And he seemed to have the faculty of always being broke.

                                    TOM MASSON.

WAKIN' THE YOUNG UNS.

SCENE.—The old man from the foot of the stairs, 5 A. M.

BEE-ULL ! Bee-ull ! O Bee-ull ! my gracious,
    Air you still sleepin'?
    Th' hour hand's creepin'
    Nearer five.
(Wal' blast it ef this ain't vexatious!)
    Don't ye hyar them cattle callin'?
    An' th' ole red steer a-bawlin'?
    Come, look alive!
        Git up ! Git up !

Mar'ann! Mar'ann! (Jist hyar her snorin'!)
    Mar'ann! it's behoovin'
    Thet you be a-movin'!
        Brisk, I say!
Hyar the kitchen stove a-roarin'?
    The kittle's a-spilin'
    To git hisse'f bilin'.
        It's comin' day.
            Git up!   Git up!

Jule, O Jule!   Now whut is ailin'?
    You want ter rest?
    Wal' I'll be blest!
        S'pose them cows
'Ll give down 'ithout you pailin'?
    You mus' be goin' crazy;
    Er, more like, gittin lazy.
        Come, now, rouse!
            Git up!   Git up!

Jake, you lazy varmint! Jake! Hey, Jake!
    What you layin' theer fer?
    You know the stock's ter keer fer;
        So, hop out!
(Thet boy is wusser'n a rock ter wake!)
    Don't stop to shiver,
    But jist unkiver,
        An' pop out!
            Git up!   Git up!

Young uns! Bee-ull! Jake! Mar'ann! Jule!
    (Wal blast my orn'ry skin!
    They've gone ter sleep agin,
        Fer all my tellin'!)

See hyar, I hain't no time ter fool!
   It's the las' warnin'
   I'll give this mornin'.
     I'm done yellin'!
      Git up!   Git up!

Wal' whut's th' odds—an hour, more or less?
   B'lieve it makes 'em stronger
   Ter sleep a leetle longer
    Thar in bed.
The times is comin' fas' enough, I guess,
   When I'll wish, an' wish 'ith weepin',
   They was back up yender sleepin',
    Overhead,
     Ter git up.

                     JOHN BOSS.

NAMING THE CHICKENS.

THERE were two little chickens hatched out by one hen,
   And the owner of both was our little boy Ben;
So he set him to work as soon as they came,
To make them a house and find them a name.

As for building a house, Benny knew very well
That he couldn't do that; but his big brother Phil
Must be handy at tools, for he'd been to college,
Where boys are supposed to learn all sorts of knowledge.

Phil was very good-natured, and soon his small brother
Had a nice cozy home for his chicks and their mother;
And a happier boy in the country just then
Could not have been found than our dear little Ben.

But a name for his pets it was harder to find;
At least, such as suited exactly his mind;

No mother of twins was ever more haunted
With trouble to find just the ones that she wanted.

There were plenty of names, no doubt about that;
But a name that would do for a dog or a cat
Would not answer for chickens so pretty as these;
Or else our dear boy was not easy to please.

These two tiny chickens looked just like each other;
To name them so young would be only a bother;
But with one in each hand, said queer little Ben:
" I want *this* one a *rooster* and *that* one a *hen.*"

Benny knew them apart by a little brown spot
On the head of the one that the other had not.
They grew up like magic, each fat, feathered chick,
One at length was named Peggy and the other named Dick.

But a funny thing happened concerning their names;
Rushing into the house one day, Benny exclaims:
"O mother! O Phil! such a blunder there's been,
For *Peggy's* the *rooster* and *Dick* is the *hen!*"

MRS. L. B. BACON.

NEEDLES AND PINS.

'WHEN will you marry me, my bonnie maid?"
　　"Can we not wait?" said she—
'You know that I love you, but dear, I'm afraid
　　You soon will get weary of me."
Then he vowed and swore to love and adore,
　　He prayed on his bended knee,
He said with a sigh "If I wait I shall die!"—
　　He was a man, you see.
Sugar and cream, sugar and cream,
When we are married 'twill be a sweet dream! } *Repeat.*

But the sugar and cream they passed like a dream,
  Alas! they could never agree.
She said, "Let us part, you've broken my heart!"
  "I think it is best," said he—
"When I'm gone you will miss me a thousand times o'er!"
  "Oh no! not a whit!" said he—
Then away she went stamping and slamming the door—
  She was a woman, you see.
Needles and pins! Needles and pins!   } *Repeat.*
When a man's married, his trouble begins!

Five minutes, precisely five minutes had passed,
  She opened the door with a sigh,
"Since we have settled to part," she said—
  "I wanted to say good-by!"
"We never shall meet any more," she wept—
  "Alone we must live and die."
Then he opened his arms and in them she crept,
  And that's how they said good-by.
Let the bells ring! Let the bells ring!   } *Repeat.*
Man without woman is but a poor thing!

TOO PROGRESSIVE FOR HIM.

I AM somethin' of a vet'ran, just a-turnin' eighty year,—
  A man that's hale and hearty an' a stranger tew all fear;
  But I've heard some news this mornin' that has made my old
    head spin,
An' I'm goin' tew ease my conshuns if I never speak ag'in.

I've lived my fourscore years of life, an' never till tew-day
Wuz I taken for a jackass or an ign'rant kind o' jay,
Tew be stuffed with such durned nonsense 'about them crawling bugs
    and worms
That's killin' human bein's with their "mikroscopic germs."

They say there's "mikrobes" all about a-lookin' for their prey;
There's nothin' pure to eat nor drink, an' no safe place to stay;
There's "miasmy" in the dewfall an' "malary" in the sun;
'Tain't safe to be outdoors at noon or when the day is done.

There's "bactery" in the water an' "trikeeny" in the meat,
"Ameeby" in the atmosphere, "calory" in the heat;
There's "corpussels" an' "pigments" in a human bein's blood,
An' every other kind o' thing existin' sence the flood.

Terbacker's full o' "nickerteen," whatever that may be;
An' your mouth'll all get puckered with the "tannin" in the tea;
The butter's "olymargareen"—it never saw a cow;
An' things is gittin' wus an' wus from what they be just now.

Them bugs is all about us, just a-waitin' fer a chance
Tew navigate our vitals an' tew naw us off like plants.
There's men that spends a lifetime huntin' worms just like a goose,
An' tackin' Latin names to 'em an' lettin' on 'em loose.

Now, I don't believe sech nonsense, an' I'm not a goin' tew try.
If things has come tew such a pass, I'm satisfied tew die;
I'll go hang me in the sullar, fer I won't be such a fool
As to wait until I'm pizened by a "annymallycool."

Lurana W. Sheldon.

THE LOW-BACK CAR.

WHEN first I saw Peggy,
    'Twas on a market day:
A low-backed car she drove, and sat
    Upon a truss of hay;
But when that hay was blooming grass,
    And decked with flowers of spring,
No flower was there that could compare
    With the blooming girl I sing.

As she sat in the low-backed car,
The man at the turnpike bar
    Never asked for the toll,
    But just rubbed his owld poll,
And looked after the low-backed car.

In battle's wild commotion,
    The proud and mighty Mars
With hostile scythes demands his tithes
    Of death in warlike cars;
While Peggy, peaceful goddess,
    Has darts in her bright eye,
That knock men down in the market town
    As right and left they fly;
While she sits in her low-backed car,
Than battle more dangerous far——
    For the doctor's art
    Cannot cure the heart
That is hit from that low-backed car.

Sweet Peggy round her car, sir,
    Has strings of ducks and geese,
But the scores of hearts she slaughters
    By far outnumber these;
While she among her poultry sits,
    Just like a turtle dove,
Well worth the cage, I do engage,
    Of the blooming god of love!
While she sits in her low-backed car,
The lovers come near and far,
    And envy the chicken
    That Peggy is pickin'
As she sits in her low-backed car.

O, I'd rather own that car, sir,
   With Peggy by my side,
Than a coach and four, and gold galore,
   And a lady for my bride;
For the lady would sit forninst me,
   On a cushion made with taste—
While Peggy would sit beside me,
   With my arm around her waist,
While we drove in the low-backed car,
To be married by Father Mahar;
   O, my heart would beat high
   At her glance and her sigh—
Though it beat in a low-backed car!

SAMUEL LOVER.

THE OLD FISHERMAN.

HE was old and weather-beaten, and his clothes were the same, but there was an expression of supreme content upon his tanned face as he sat on the edge of the wharf yesterday afternoon and let his legs dangle down. In his mouth was a pipe that had been new and sweet in the dear, dead long ago, and in his right hand he held one end of a fish-line. The other end was held down upon the bottom of the river, a long distance from the shore.

"Any luck, captain?" asked a young man who was strolling by. It is considered the proper thing to call every man along the river who is old and weather beaten "captain."

"Nope—they an't a-bitin' much to-day."

"They don't bite much anyway these days, do they?"

"Nope—not like they useter. 'Tuseter be so't I could come aown here an' catch a basketful in mebbe an hour or so."

"That was quite long ago, wasn't it?"

"Yep, quite a spell ago. I 'member one time—hello!"

The old man had given his line a vicious jerk and was now all excitement.

"Got a bite, captain?"

"Yep, an' he's a whopper, too. I ain't quite sure whether I've hooked him. Yep, there he is. I feel him a-wigglin' on the line. He's a great, big, striped bass."

All this was said in a sort of stage whisper.

"How do you know what kind of a fish it is?"

"How do I know?" repeated the old man, as he began slowly and deliberately to haul in his line, and he threw supreme pity for the ignorance implied by the question into his voice. "How do I know? Why, young man, I can tell jes' what kind of a fish 'tis by the way he bites. Now, there's an eel; he kind o' makes little bits o' pecks at yer line, an' then he takes holt an' swims away with yer line sort o' easy like. Then there's the sucker; he jes' sucks yer bait, an' ye can't hardly feel him pull. An' then there's the yellow perch; he takes holt right away and swims away like a streak."

"And how does the striped bass bite?" interrupted the young man.

"Oh, he monkeys around a whole lot, and then he takes hold all of a sudden and swims away down stream. I knowed right away when this fellow took holt he was a striped bass. I never make no mistake. I——"

Just then the old man's catch came to the surface. It was an old boot.

KITTENS AND BABIES.

THERE were two kittens, a black and a gray,
    And grandmamma said, with a frown,
"It never will do to keep them both,
    The black one we'd better drown."

"Don't cry, my dear," to tiny Bess,
    "One kitten's enough to keep;
Now run to nurse, for 'tis growing late,
    And time you were fast asleep."

The morrow dawned, and rosy and sweet
   Came little Bess from her nap.
The nurse said, " Go into mamma's room
   And look in grandma's lap."

" Come here," said grandma, with a smile,
   From the rocking-chair where she sat.
" God has sent you two little sisters ;
   Now ! What do you think of that ? "

Bess looked at the babies a moment,
   With their wee heads, yellow and brown,
And then to grandma, soberly said,
   " Which one are you going to drown ? "

A SIMILAR CASE.

WELL, Jack !   Hear you've gone and done it—
   Yes, I know most fellows will.
   Went and tried it once myself, sir,
     Though, you see, I'm single still.
And you met her, did you—tell me—
   Down at Newport, last July,
And resolved to ask the question
   At a soiree !   So did I.

I suppose you left the ball room
   With its music and its light—
For they say love's flame is brightest
   In the darkness of the night.
Well, you walked along together,
   Overhead the starlit sky,
And I'll bet, old man, confess it !
   You were frightened.   So was I.

Then you strolled along the terrace,
  Saw the summer moonlight pour
All its radiance on the waters
  As they rippled on the shore.
Till at length you gathered courage,
  When you saw that none were nigh,
And you drew her close and told her
  That you loved her.   So did I.

Well, I needn't ask you further,
  And I'm sure I wish you joy.
Think I'll wander down to see you
  When your married.   Eh! my boy?
When the honeymoon is over,
  And you're settled down, we'll try—
What!   The deuce you say—rejected?
  You rejected?   So was *I!*

A FLY'S COGITATIONS.

I WONDER what this man is doing? I'll just light on his bald head and see what is going on in his thinkery. What! Now, I wonder what he slapped his pate so savagely for? Why, the man must be crazy. I went away just as quick as I saw him raise his hand. Really, he could not complain of that. Maybe he thought I was intruding; but, if so, he cannot say but that I lit out at his first hint. But he seems quiet enough now. Maybe his scalp itched or something, and his move had no reference to my being on it, so I guess I will try it again. What a nice old bald head this is, to be sure, only it's its a trifle slippery. It would make a first-rate skating-rink; guess I will try it. Whew! Why, the man hit his head again.

Funny way he has with him; and, if I hadn't got out of the way just as I did, goodness only knows what might have happened to me. He struck real hard, and if he had hit me, there is no knowing, but that he might have hurt me. But, maybe he hadn't any idea of hitting me. I guess I'll just light on his nose and see what the matter is with him. What! Why he seems to be an awfully sensitive sort of a man, or else he has got a dreadful temper. Why, he actually hit his own nose a slap just because I crawled around on it a bit. Queer sort of a chap, anyway. Wonder if he thinks a fly has no rights in this world.

Now, I will try him in the ear. Ah! I have got him now! Good gracious! he came within an ace of hitting me that time. Wonder what he means, anyhow? I should think he was mad about something. I'll try his other ear and see how he likes that. Ah! he don't seem to mind this one so much. Ah! by Jingoes, he must have hurt himself that time with that bat on the ear. But it's his ear, not mine, so what should I care?

I think I'll fly around the room! See him flop and fling his arms around as though the air was full of flying demons. Funny, isn't it? He don't see me up here, but he is looking wildly around as though he wanted to fight somebody. Oh! I'll just try his temper a bit further; I'll get on where his hair is short behind. Ah! I'll fool around here in this stubble awhile. Now he flops his handkerchief, but I don't care for that. I can get away from a demonstration of that kind every time.

Now I have got h.... on the ear again, and once more he paws the air in the immediate vicinity, but I am out of harm's way, ha! ha! Now he is red in the face; yes, he looks like a boiled lobster, and again he is dancing around the room and swearing like a trooper! Now he has quieted down a trifle and has resumed writing again! Ah! he smiles! Must be he has got on to an idea. I wonder what it is? I'll just take a quiet walk over that thinkery again, and maybe I can catch on to what it is. What in the world is he making his scalp go this way for? I would think he was trying to shake something off. Oh! I'll just get a grip on here and hold on for awhile. No, he can't shake me off; no, no! Ah ——!

There was a resounding whack—that lively fly, oh where was he? Dead!

JUST AT DUSK A HORSE OF BROWN, FLECKED WITH FOAM, CAME
PANTING DOWN

THE RIDE OF PAUL VENARES

THE DAUGHTER OF THE REGIMENT—Suggestion for a tableau

THE CHARGE ON "OLD HUNDRED."

HALF a bar, half a bar,
Half a bar onward!
Into an awful ditch,
Choir and precentor hitch,
Into a mess of pitch
They led the Old Hundred.

Trebles to right of them,
Tenors to left of them,
Basses in front of them,
Bellowed and thundered.
Oh! that precentor's look,
When the sopranos took
Their own time and hook,
From the Old Hundred.

Screeched all the trebles here,
Boggled the tenors there,
Raising the parson's hair,
While his mind wandered;
Theirs not to reason why
This psalm was pitched too high;
Theirs but to gasp and cry
Out the Old Hundred.

Trebles to right of them,
Tenors to left of them,
Basses in front of them,
Bellowed and thundered.
Stormed they with shout and yell,
Not wise they sang, nor well,
Drowning the sexton's bell,
While all the church wondered.

Dire the precentor's glare,
Flashed his pitchfork in air,
Sounding fresh keys to bear
        Out the Old Hvndred.
Swiftly he turned his back,
Reached he his hat from rack,
Then from the screaming pack
        Himself he sundered.

Tenors to right of him,
Trebles to left of him,
Discords behind him,
        Bellowed and thundered.
Oh, the wild howls they wrought;
Right to the end they fought!
Some tune they sung, but not,
        Not the Old Hundred.

A MARRIED LOVE-LETTER.

YOUR letter was received, dear John, I write as you request,
        And send the white-winged tidings from our little love-built
        nest.
We miss you sadly, night and morn.   That odious Mr. Dent
Has called at least a dozen times to dun you for the rent.

You say it seems an age, my love, since last you went away;
But then it's quite a comfort, dear, to know the trip will pay.
We're saving every penny we can, and living very plain;
I had my pocket picked last night, while walking through the rain.

You count the lagging hours, dear, that keep you from my side;
For, as you fondly say, the wife is dearer than the bride.
That Miss Modiste has sent her bill, I know you'll be amazed;
I never got one-half the things—the creature must be crazed!

The children—precious little pets!—ask daily for papa.
They all have had such shocking colds, I called in Doctor Law.
He fears that Nettie's lungs are weak—she seems inclined to stoop;
The baby has the nettle rash, and Sammy chronic croup.

And, oh! Mamma and Mr. B. have had an awful fuss;
Of course, she couldn't stay at Em's, and so she's here with us.
The girls have "given warning," love; I don't know what to think
Unless, as dear mamma suspects, they're both inclined to drink.

I'm feeling sad, and far from well, but then, I know, dear John,
A long home-letter, just like this, will cheer and help you on.
I'd like to nestle to your breast and have a hearty cry;
Pray don't forget the grocer's bill! God bless your love! Good-by!

THE RULING PASSION.

SHE had never mailed a letter before, and so she approached the stamp clerk's window with the same air that she would enter a dry-goods store.

"I would like to look at some stamps, please," she said.

"What denomination do you want?" asked the clerk.

"Denomination!" This was remarked in surprise. She hadn't supposed that stamps belonged to any church at all.

"Yes," replied the clerk, who saw no necessity for holding a lengthy palaver over the sale of a stamp, especially when other people were waiting. "Is it for a letter or a newspaper?"

"O, I want to send a letter to my Uncle John; he's just moved to——"

"Then you need a two-cent stamp," interrupted the clerk, offering her one of that value.

"I hardly like that color," she observed, holding the brick-tinted stamp up to the light and surveying it critically.

The clerk looked at her in astonishment. In his long experience in the postal business he had never before met a customer who objected to the color of the stamps.

" That is a two-cent stamp, madam. Please stand aside, and let the gentleman behind you come up."

" Haven't you got them in any other color ? " she asked, wholly oblivious to the " gentleman behind."

The clerk began to act cross.

" I never did like that shade of red," she added.

" There is only one color," he replied curtly.

" That is strange," she mused. " I'd think you'd keep them in different shades, so that there'd be some choice."

The clerk said nothing, but he kept getting crosser every minute, and murmurs of disapprobation began to rise from the ever-lengthening line of people who would have been thankful to get their stamps without criticising their hue.

" You are sure you have none in a brighter red, or even in a different color—Nile green, or seal brown, or jubliee blue, for instance ? "

" You can put two one-cent stamps on your letter if you like," said the clerk, who began to see that the customer could not be frowned away from the window.

" Let me see them, please."

" Two blue stamps were solemnly handed to her, and the crowd began to hope that at last she was suited.

" Ah, that will do," she said, as she took up the one-cent stamps and eyed them as if they were samples of dress goods. " I like that shade better. I'll take only one, if you please."

And she handed the other back to the clerk, who took it mechanically, but managed to add :

" If it's for a letter you'll need two. These are one-cent stamps and letter postage is two cents per ounce."

" Oh, I don't want to put two stamps on my letter," she said; " I don't think they will look well."

" It requires two cents to carry a letter, madam, and you must either put a two-cent stamp on or two ones. It won't go without.

And I must ask you to please hurry, for you are keeping a great many people away from the window."

"That's singular. I don't like the looks of two together. You are sure the other doesn't come in seal-brown, or——"

"No!" thundered the clerk, getting very red in the face.

"Then I'll have to see if I can't suit myself elsewhere."

And she departed.

The clerk replaced his despised red and blue stamps, mopped his perspiring brow, and began to make up for lost time.—WM. H. SWITER.

A COMPLAINT.

I THINK it really mean—don't you?—
　　To leave us nothing at all to do!
　　In a world all made to order so
A modern boy has no earthly show.
Columbus sailed across the sea,
Which might have been done by you or me,
And now they call him great and wise,
They praise his genius and enterprise,
Although when he found our native land,
He took it for India's coral strand!
There's noble George who wouldn't lie—
Perhaps he couldn't. He didn't try.
But if I should cut down a cherry-tree,
My father would only laugh at me.

Benjamin Franklin—what did *he* do?
Flew a big kite; on Sunday, too,
Standing out in a heavy shower
Getting soaked for half an hour,
Fishing for lightning with a string
To see if he couldn't bottle the thing.
Suppose I should fly my kite in the rain?

People would say that I wasn't sane.
Why should there such a difference be
Between Ben Franklin, Esquire, and me?

I can see steam move a kettle-lid
Quite as well as James Watt did,
And I can explain about engines, too,
Bigger and better than Watt ever knew:
But somehow he took all the praise,
And I'm neglected nowadays.

Still, what makes me feel the worst
Is Adam's renown for being first.
That was easy enough, you know;
It was just a thing that happened so.
And my sister says, " If it had been *me*
I wouldn't have touched the apple-tree."
That's so.   If she sees a snake to-day,
She gives a scream and she scoots away.

To write such things as Shakespeare's plays
Was not so hard in Queen Bess's days,
But now, when everything has been done,
I cannot think of a single one
To bring a boy to wealth and fame,
It's a regular, downright, burning shame!

P. S.—When it's fine I shall play base-ball;
For you know it never would do at all
To forget about " Jack " who becomes, they say,
A very dull boy, without plenty of play.
But, wait!—when a rainy Saturday comes,
As soon as I've finished Monday's sums,
I'm going to build a great flying-machine
That will make T. Edison look pea-green!

                              B. A. PENNYPACKER

SUNDAY TALK N THE HORSE SHEDS.

[Old Gray comments on the service to his mate.]

'TISN'T so much that the Sunday harness never seems to fit,
    That the collar is ight, an' the check-rein draws on this queer
        new-fangle l bit,
Nor yet that the pasture looks greener, somehow, this sort of a half-
        rest day,
That galls me most, Old Roan, but the things I hear the people say.

My shoulders ache, an' my knees are stiff, an' it makes me want to
        fight
When I hear 'em sing, " O Day of Rest ! O Day of Joy an' Light ! "
For we startled late, an' to get here soon we had to trot our best ;
" Welcome "—now hear 'em—" delightful morn, sweet day of sacred
        rest ! "

Now parson's readin' the Scripture, " Remember the Sabbath day—
In it thou shalt not do any work "—" Amen," the people say ;
" Thou, nor thy son, nor thy daughter, thy cattle, thy ox, nor thy
        ass "—
Don't seem to exempt the horses, eh ?   So we'll let the lesson pass.

Can't you step over a little ?   The sun comes in this side—
An' it don't say a word about the wife ; I reckon that's why they
        decide
That Sunday's a day of rest on the farm from the labors of every-day
        life
For everything that the Lord hath made—except the horses an' wife.

Now, that's our hymn ; come, wake up, Roan, that means us, I'll be
        bound—
" Awake, my soul "—sing louder'n that ; some folks sleep mighty
        sound—
" Awake, my soul, an' with the sun "—that's meant for me an' you—
" Thy daily course of duty run "—well, that's just what we do.

" A righteous man regardeth the life of his beast "—I'd smile
At the parson's text, but if I did they' hear me for a mile ;
For I trotted the last ten minutes lame—I'd picked up a hard, sharp
     stone,
An' could hear the old man growlin' because his seat was " hard as a
     bone."

" Could I but climb where Moses stood "—but the half of them
     wouldn't climb ;
They'd pile in the wagon full's 'twould hold an' ride up every time ;
If they had to walk they'd do's they did when your pastern joint was
     sprained—
They'd say 'twas too far, an' stay at home, like they did the times it
     rained.

I'm goin' to write a hymn some day, an' we'll sing it out in the sheds—
" Welcome, delightful morn that pours the rain upon our heads ;
Welcome the slush, the snow that drifts, the mud that irritates,
The storms that bring a Sabbath rest to the cattle within the gates."

His voice was hushed, for the notes of song rose on the hallowed air—
" Praise God from whom all blessings flow "—thanksgiving, praise
     and prayer ;
" Praise Him all creatures here below "—man, beast, an' bird an'
     thing—
With the possible exception of the farmer's wife, who, having remained
     at home to prepare a dinner of chicken soup, roast beef, beets,
     onions, roasting ears, salad, pudding, two kinds of pie and
     fruit for her husband, three sons, four daughters, the pastor,
     his wife and two children, the district secretary of the Home
     Mission Society, a distant relative from the city come out to
     spend the day, and two hired men, had very little time, and not
     much breath, and possibly not an everlastingly superabundant
     inclination to sing.

                             ROBERT J. BURDETTE.

WE ALL KNOW HER.

SHE warbled the soprano with dramatic sensibility,
  And dallied with the organ when the organist was sick;
She got up for variety a brand-new church society, and
  Spoke with great facility about the new church brick.

She shed great tears of sorrow for the heathen immorality,
  And organized a system that would open up their eyes;
In culinary clarity she won great popularity, and
  Showed her personality in lecturing on pies.

For real unvarnished culture she betrayed a great propensity;
  Her Tuesday-talks were famous and her Friday-glimmers great.
She grasped at electricity with mental elasticity
  And lectured with intensity about the marriage state.

But with the calm assurance of her wonderful capacity,
  She wouldn't wash the dishes, but she'd talk all day on rocks;
And while she dwelt on density, or space and its immensity,
  With such refined audacity, her mother darned the socks!

TOM MASON.

TOO BAD.

NOTHING to do but work,
  Nothing to eat but food,
Nothing to wear but clothes
  To keep one from going nude.

Nothing to breathe but air;
  Quick as a flash 'tis gone;
Nowhere to fall but off,
  Nowhere to stand but on.

Nothing to comb but hair,
   Nowhere to sleep but in bed,
Nothing to weep but tears,
   Nothing to bury but dead.

Nothing to sing but songs,
   Ah, well, alas! Alack!
Nowhere to go but out,
   Nowhere to come but back.

Nothing to see but sights,
   Nothing to quench but thirst,
Nothing to have but what we've got,
   Thus through life we are cursed.

Nothing to strike but a gait,
   Everything moves that goes.
Nothing at all but common sense
   Can ever withstand these woes.

THE WRONG TRAIN.

WE had been to town-meeting, had once voyaged a hundred miles on a steamboat and had a brother who had made the overland trip to California.

She had been to quiltings, funerals, and a circus or two; and she knew a woman who thought nothing of setting out on a railroad journey where she had to wait fifteen minutes at a junction and change cars at a depot.

So I found them,—a cosy-looking old couple, sitting up very straight in their seat, and trying to act like old railroad travellers. A shadow of anxiety suddenly crossed her face; she became uneasy, and directly she asked:

"Philetus, I act'lly b'lieve we've went and took the wrong train!"

"It can't be, nohow," he replied, seeming a little startled. "Didn't I ask the conductor, and he said we was right?"

"Yaas, he did; but look out the window, and make sure. He might have been lyin' to us."

The old man looked out the window at the flitting fences, the galloping telegraph-poles, and the unfamiliar fields, as if expecting to catch sight of some landmark, and forgetting for a moment that he was a thousand miles from home.

"I guess we're all right, Mary," he said, as he drew in his head.

"Ask somebody—ask that man there," she whispered.

"This is the train for Chicago, hain't it?" inquired the old man of the passenger in the next seat behind.

"This is the train," replied the man.

"There! didn't I say so!" clucked the old gent.

"It may be--it may be!" she replied, dubiously; "but if we are carried wrong, it won't be my fault. I say that we are wrong, and when we've been led into some pirate's cave, and butchered for our money, ye'll wish ye had heeded my words!"

He looked out of the window again, opened his mouth as if to make some inquiry of a boy sitting on the fence, and then leaned back on his seat and sighed heavily. She shut her teeth together, as if saying that she could stand it if he could, and the train sped along for several miles. He finally said:

"Looks like rain over thar in the west. I hope the boys have got them oats in."

"That makes me think of the umbreller!" diving her hands among the parcels at their feet.

She hunted around two or three minutes, growing red in the face, and then straightened up and hoarsely whispered:

"It's gone!"

"W—what?" he gasped.

"That umbreller!"

"No!"

"Gone, hide and hair!" so she went on, "that sky-blue umbreller, which I've had ever since Martha died."

He searched around, but it was not to be found.

"Waal, thar's queer," he mused, as he straightened up.

"Queer! not a bit. I've talked to ye and talked to ye, but it does no good. Ye come from a heedless fam'ly; and ye'd forget to put on your boots, 'f I didn't tell ye to."

"None of the Harrisons was ever in the poor-house!" he replied, in a cutting tone.

"Philetus! Philetus H. Harrison!" she continued, laying her hand on his arm, "don't you dare twit me of that again! I've lived with ye nigh on to forty years and waited on ye when ye had biles and the toothache and the colic, and when ye fell and broke your leg; but don't push me up to the wall!"

He looked out of the window, feeling that she had the advantage of him, and she wiped her eyes, settled her glasses on her nose, and used up the next fifteen minutes in thinking of the past. Feeling thirsty, she reached down among the bundles, searched around, and her face was as pale as death as she straightened back and whispered—

"And that's gone, too!"

"What now?" he asked,

"It's been stole!" she exclaimed, looking around the car, as if expecting to see some one with the bottle to his lips.

"Fust the umbreller—then the bottle!" she gasped.

"I couldn't have left it, could I?"

"Don't ask me! That bottle has been in our family twenty years, ever since mother died; and now it's gone! Land only knows what I'll do for a camfire bottle when we git home, if we ever do!"

"I'll buy one."

"Yes, I know ye are always ready to buy; and if it wasn't for me to restrain ye, the money'd fly likefeathers in the wind."

"Waal, I didn't have to mortgage my farm," he replied, giving her a knowing look.

"Twitting agin? It isn't enough that you've lost a good umbreller and a camfire bottle; but you must twit me o' this and that."

Her nose grew red, and tears came to her eyes; but as he was looking out of the window, she said nothing further Ten or fifteen minutes passed; and, growing restless, he called out to a man across the aisle.

"What's the sile around here?"

"Philetus! Philetus H. Harrison! stop your noise!" she whispered, poking him with her elbow.

"I just asked a question," he replied, resuming his old position.

"What'd your brother Joab tell ye, the last thing afore we left him hum?" she asked. "Didn't he say somebody'd swindle ye on the string game, the confidence game, or some other game? Didn't he warn ye agin rascals?"

"I hain't seen no rascals."

"Of course, ye haven't, 'cause yer blind! I know that man is a villun; and if they don't arrest him for murder afore we leave this train, I'll miss my guess. I can read human-natur' like a book."

There was another period of silence, broken by her saying:

"I wish I knew that this was the train for Chicago."

"'Course it is."

"How do you know?"

"'Cause it is."

"Waal, I know it hain't; but if you are contented to rush along to your destruction, I shan't say a word. Only when yer throat is being cut, don't call out that I didn't warn ye!"

The peanut boy came along, and the old man reached down for his wallet.

"Philetus, ye shan't squander that money after peanuts!" she exclaimed, using the one hand to catch his arm, and the other to wave the boy on.

"Didn't I earn it?"

"Yaas, you sold two cows to get money to go on this visit; but it's half gone now, and the land only knows how we'll get home!"

The boy walked on, and the flag of truce was hung out for another brief time. She recommenced hostilities by remarking:

"I wish I hadn't cum."

He looked up, and then out of the window.

"I know what ye want to say," she hissed; "but it's a blessed good thing for you that I did come! If ye'd come alone, ye'd have been murdered and gashed and scalped, and sunk into the river afore now!"

"Pooh!"

"Yes, pooh, 'f you want to, but I know!"

He leaned back; she settled herself anew; and by and by—

He nodded—she nodded. And in sleep their gray heads touched; and his arm found its way along the back of the seat, and his hand rested on her shoulder.—M. QUAD.

HOW FATHER CARVES THE DUCK.

WE all look on with anxious eyes,
　　When father carves the duck,
　　And mother almost always sighs,
　　When father carves the duck.
Then all of us prepare to rise
And hold our bibs before our eyes
And be prepared for some surprise,
　　When father carves the duck.

He braces up and grabs a fork,
　　Whene'er he carves a duck,
And won't allow a soul to talk,
　　Until he carves the duck.
The fork is jabbed into the sides,
Across the breast the knife he slides,
While every careful person hides
　　From flying chips of duck.

The platter's always sure to slip,
　　When father carves the duck.
And how it makes the dishes skip!

Potatoes fly amuck.
The squash and cabbage leap in space,
And father mutters Hindoo grace,
Whene'er he carves a duck.

We all have learned to walk around
The dining-room, and pluck
From off the window-sills and walls
Our share of father's duck,
While father growls and blows and jaws,
And swears the knife is full of flaws.
And mother jeers at him, because
He cannot carve a duck.

THE MEN WHO DO NOT LIFT.

THE world is sympathetic; the statement none can doubt.
When A's in trouble don't we think that B should help him
out?
Of course, we haven't time ourselves to care for any one,
But yet we hope that other folks will see that it is done.
We want the grief and penury of earth to be relieved;
We'd have the battles grandly fought, the victories achieved;
We do not care to take the lead, and stand the brush and brunt;
At lifting we're a failure, but we're splendid on the grunt.

And there are others, so we find, as on our way we jog,
Who want to do their lifting on the small end of the log;
They do a lot of blowing, and they strive to make it known
That were there no one else to help, they'd lift it all alone.
If talking were effective, there are scores and scores of men
Who'd move a mountain off its base and move it back again.
But as a class, to state it plain, in language true and blunt,
They're never worth a cent to lift, for all they do is grunt.